H. 35 P. Biograp[...]

5255-46

HH/59

add "Lancaster Co. Va. +
far beyond —"

In pub near fire place.

3L-7

LANDON CARTER PAPERS

THE

LANDON CARTER PAPERS

in the

University of Virginia Library

A Calendar and Biographical Sketch

BY

WALTER RAY WINEMAN

UNIVERSITY OF VIRGINIA PRESS

CHARLOTTESVILLE, 1962

Printed by The William Byrd Press, Inc. on Standard Permalife Text

CONTENTS

FOREWORD

THE HISTORICAL SIGNIFICANCE of Colonel Landon Carter of "Sabine Hall" has been generally overlooked by Americans who live outside tidewater Virginia. As a member of the Carter family and a representative of eighteenth-century Virginia society, his position has been overshadowed by that of his father, Robert "King" Carter, and by that of his nephew, Robert Carter of "Nomini Hall." In the political field, Landon Carter had neither the opportunity nor the desire to serve in the highest echelon of colonial government, so that his name does not appear prominently in the records of his period. During the Revolution his conservative views prevented him from becoming a popular figure.

It was in the struggle for liberty, however, that Colonel Carter made his greatest public contribution. Two related factors explain the minor place he has been given in the popular histories of his day. In the first place, his most important influence was exerted through his correspondence, his published articles, and his phrasing of official statements. A full appreciation of his worth depends, therefore, upon the identification and study of the drafts of these letters and documents, many of which were written anonymously or signed fictitiously.

Secondly, once the colonial desire for justice and fair treatment as Englishmen had developed into a demand for independence, it was neither safe nor reasonable for an obstinate conservative like Colonel Carter to express his views in public. Instead, he used his influence for moderation privately, the records of his views and activities being confined largely to his diary and private papers.

Only recently has it been possible for anyone other than the Carter family to study these papers. In 1943 the present heir of

Landon Carter deposited the papers relating to the "Sabine Hall" estate with the Manuscripts Division of the Alderman Library at the University of Virginia. Shortly thereafter the papers were restored and made ready for study.

Before the papers can be used effectively as a source of information, however, it is necessary that the items be identified and their relationship to each other be indicated. The effort to prepare such a calendar is the principal purpose of the present study.

Because most of the papers relate directly to Landon Carter, in order to prepare the calendar and to make it usable to others, adequate biographical material is needed. A biographical sketch is included as Part Two of the present study to supply this information.

By necessity as well as by design, the major sources of the information in the sketch have been the manuscripts in the Sabine Hall Collection, including the Landon Carter Diary, and the official records of colonial Virginia and of the counties of Richmond and Lancaster. Additional primary material was found in the manuscript files of the Virginia Historical Society, and photostats of some of the documents in the Carter Collection at Duke University. The bound volumes of the *Virginia Gazette* and the published correspondence of the prominent men of the period furnished further information.

I wish to express my appreciation to the Reverend Dabney Wellford for permitting me to use the manuscripts in the Sabine Hall Collection. To Miss Anne Freudenberg, Assistant Curator of Manuscripts at the University of Virginia's Alderman Library, I am greatly indebted for her generous undertaking in compiling the index to the calendar. For their advice and guidance, I wish to thank also Miss Freudenberg's associates, Mr. Francis L. Berkeley, Jr., Mr. Russell M. Smith, Mr. Robert E. Stocking, and Mr. William H. Runge.

WALTER R. WINEMAN

San Diego State College
April, 1962

PART ONE

CALENDAR OF THE LANDON CARTER PAPERS
IN THE SABINE HALL COLLECTION

I

INTRODUCTION

THE LANDON CARTER PAPERS calendared here constitute the first section of the Sabine Hall Collection of manuscripts at the Alderman Library of the University of Virginia. The Collection was deposited with the University in 1943 by the Rev. Dabney Wellford, Carter heir and present owner of Sabine Hall.

The decision to conclude this calendar with the last item in the collection related to Landon Carter (1710-1778) was made for the advantage of those interested in eighteenth-century Virginia and those specifically interested in Colonel Carter himself. The initial items are land papers of the late seventeenth century which predate the Colonel, but have been included because they constitute the basis of his claims to his property.

Over the years a number of the Sabine Hall manuscripts have been sold to interested parties and have become included in other collections. In 1889 Robert Carter Wellford sold several lots of letters to Cassius Francis Lee, Jr. of Arlington, Virginia. These included letters from George Washington, Richard Henry Lee, and his brother, Francis Lightfoot Lee. According to present accounts, C. F. Lee, Jr., during his lifetime, gave these papers to appropriate historical organizations. The individual letters were not identified in the correspondence relative to the original sale, and for this reason the present location of the letters cannot be positively determined.

In 1892 Robert Carter Wellford sold a group of 49 letters from the collection to William F. Havemeyer of New York. These letters were written between 1735 and 1777 by some of the leading political leaders of Virginia and apparently were addressed to Colonel Landon Carter. Again, the individual letters included in the sale were not identified, therefore their positive location since the death of William Havemeyer in 1913 is not certain.

Another sale of Sabine Hall manuscripts was concluded in 1935 between A. N. Wellford and Dr. E. G. Swem of the College of William and Mary. Included in this sale were a number of items relating to Landon Carter written between 1729 and 1778. At the present time an inventory of manuscripts in the possession of the College of William and Mary includes 43 Landon Carter items.

Also on deposit at the University of Virginia is Landon Carter's personal diary, which he maintained from 1752 until the time of his death in 1778. This diary appears to have been kept irregularly through the years with the entries in some cases being made in neat journal books, in other cases being made on the blank pages of magazines and pamphlets.

In addition to the diary items at the University of Virginia are a number of items acquired by William L. Clements sometime prior to 1923 and now included in the manuscript collection of the William L. Clements Library at the University of Michigan. These entries of the diary covering the periods from March 8 to October 27, 1766 and from January 9 to March 16, 1767 were written on blank pages of the *Virginia Almanac* for those years. The diary is at present being edited by Dr. Jack P. Greene for publication by The Virginia Historical Society.

The entries in the Calendar have been arranged chronologically, and each item has been accompanied by a parenthetical number for reference purposes. Each entry contains two paragraphs. In the first an effort has been made to include all pertinent names, dates, addresses or locations, type of manuscript (letter or document, and whether in the autograph of the signer), and the number of pages. The second paragraph is a summary of the contents of the item and contains references to related entries; it also includes comments indicating the manner in which the item is related to others in the collection or to Landon Carter.

Parentheses have been used for explanatory comment. Brackets have been used to indicate insertions in direct quotations and to point up dates that were not provided in the manuscripts but which have been determined by internal evidence.

Abbreviations and symbols have been used freely, particularly in citing dates and frequently recurring names and places. Except where the name appears in direct quotation, the initials "L.C." have been used throughout in referring to the first Landon Carter, both for the sake of brevity and to distinguish him from his son, grandson, and nephew. Other abbreviations and symbols used include the following:

AD	Autograph document
ADS	Autograph document, signed
AL	Autograph letter
ALS	Autograph letter, signed
D	Document
DS	Document, signed
End.	Endorsed
L	Letter
LS	Letter, signed

II

CALENDAR

1659 Nov. 2. WILLIAM UNDER-
WOOD of Rappahannock to CAP-
TAIN RICHARD LOES and
RICE E. JONES. DS. 2 pp. Wit-
nessed by Thomas Goodrich, John
Catlett, William Underwood, and
Hum. Booth. Attested by Richard
Buckner.

Deed of sale for plantation on
the Rappahannock River and
Brushwood Creek for £120 sterling; this tract adjoined the land
of Colonel Fauntleroy and was
known as Mangorick. (It later became an important part of the
"Sabine Hall" estate; see September 4, 1738.) [1]

1664-65 Mar. 10. WILLIAM BERKE-
LEY, Lieutenant Governor of Virginia, to RICHARD WEBLEY.
DS. 2 pp. Attested by Philip Lud-
well, Clerk. Recorded in Richmond County Court January 7,
1703; attested by James Sherlock,
Clerk; certified by M[armaduke]
Beckwith.

Patent for 480 acres of land in
Rappahannock County "due to
Webley for transportation of ten
persons into the colony." (This
tract was located in that section
of Rappahannock County which

became Richmond County in
1694.) [2]

1680 Aug. 9. WALTER PAVEY to
THOMAS FULLER. DS. 2 pp.
Witnessed by Rog Hull and R.
Glover, Jr. Plat of property at-
tached.

Deed of sale of 100 acres of
land for 6,000 pounds of tobacco.
This tract was part of the Richard
Webley grant of 1664. [3]

1680-81 Jan. 3. WALTER PAVEY of
Rappahannock to JOHN RICE.
DS. 2 pp. "Acknowledged in Court
before Governor and Council."
Attested by Ed. Chilton, Clerk.
Recorded in Rappahannock
County Court Sept. 2, 1682; at-
tested by J. [Craske]; certified by
Richard Buckner.

Deed of sale for 350 acres of
land for 12,000 pounds of tobacco.
This tract was part of the 480
acres granted to Richard Webley
by Governor William Berkeley in
1664. (See March 10, 1664.) [4]

1683 June 13. WILLIAM MOSELEY,
Surveyor. ADS. 1 p. Docketed:
"Ben Hind's Plat."

Plat and description of 100 acres

of land in Rappahannock County purchased by Thomas Fuller from Walter Pavey. (See August 9, 1680.) [5]

1683 Sept. 4. WALTER PAVEY and MARY PAVEY to THOMAS FULLER. DS. 2 pp. Recorded in Rappahannock County Court Mar. 7, 1784. Attested by Wm. Colston, Clerk. Docketed. Plat attached.

Deed of sale of 100 acres of land for 6,000 pounds of tobacco. (See August 9, 1680 and June 13, 1683.) [6]

1683-84 Jan. 21. RICHARD GLOVER of Rappahannock to WALTER PAVEY. DS. 1 p. Witnessed by John Rice, J. Webb, and Jo. Taverner. Docketed. Seal intact.

Indenture of release of 150 acres of land on northern bank of Rappahannock River between the plantation of John Rice and the dwelling and cleared ground of Walter Pavey. [7]

1683-84 Jan. 28. WALTER PAVEY and MARY PAVEY to JOHN RICE. DS. 2 pp. Witnessed by J. Webb, John Galloway, and Jo. Taverner. Recorded in Rappahannock County Court April 3, 1684. Attested by William Colston, Clerk. Docketed.

Indenture: Walter and Mary Pavey agree to sell 194 acres of land in Rappahannock County for 12,000 pounds of tobacco. [8]

1683-84 Feb. 27. WILL[IAM] MOSELEY, Surveyor. ADS. 1 p. Docketed.

Survey of 1,273 acres of land lying north of Rappahannock River on Mangorick and Brushwood Creeks and owned by Colonel William Lloyd. Also fragment of Walter Pavey's deed to William Lloyd. (See ca. 1731.) [9]

1693 Oct. 6. JOHN RICE. D. 3 pp. Recorded in Richmond County Court Oct. 6, 1693. Witnessed by Cornellius O. J. Mello, Wm. R. Witt, John Pound, Jno. Kirby [?], and Walter Pavey. Copy attested by Wm. Colston, Clerk. Docketed.

Will of John Rice, former owner of part of "Sabine Hall" estate. [10]

1698 Apr. 25. JOHN CHAMPE, Richmond County, to COL. WILLIAM PIERCE. DS. 1 p. Witnessed by Mary Pierce and Sam Bayly. Recorded in Richmond County Court April 27, 1698. Copy attested by Ja. Westcomb, Clerk.

Deed of sale of small parcel of land estimated to contain 10 to 12 acres. [11]

[18th cent. early.] MAP OF SABINE HALL ESTATE. D. 1 p.

Map and description of a tract of 1,016 acres of land, showing location of a dwelling house and describing boundary points. [12]

[18th cent. early.] MAP OF SABINE HALL ESTATE. D. 2 pp.

Map of part of "Sabine Hall" estate with legend indicating some of the former purchases, noting directly the purchases of John Rice. (Area designated as "coppage" [Coppridge?] corresponds to the 100-acre tract Thomas Fuller bought from Walter Pavey, which was surveyed by William Moseley on June 13, 1683. See August 9, 1680.) [13]

[18th cent. early.] PLAT of land in [Lancaster County], surveyed by GEORGE ASHTON, Gent., for COL. ROBERT CARTER. AD. 1 p. Docketed.

(This tract appears to be Corotoman.) [14]

[18th cent. early.] FRAGMENTS.

1 cover page, addressee, "Landon Carter, Esq.," serving as notepaper for unidentified survey notations.

1 fragment of grant by George II to Captain Thomas Wright.

1 unidentified land survey. [15]

1712 Aug. 27. ROBERT CARTER, agent for Lady Catherine Fairfax, Baronness Dowager of Cameron, Scotland, Proprietor of the Northern Neck of Virginia, to SHARSHALL GRASTY of Lancaster County. DS. 2 pp. Signed by Robert Carter. Docketed. Seal intact.

Grant of 840 acres of land in Richmond and Westmoreland Counties for annual rental of ten shillings per 50 acres. On verso is assignment of this property to Robert Carter, October 14, 1713. Signed by Sharshall Grasty. Attested by Jn. Grayson, Cary Keble, and William Ranken. [16]

1713 Sept. 29. SHARSHALL GRASTY to ROBERT CARTER. DS. 2 pp. Docketed: "Sharshall Grasty's deed of conveyance for 840 acres of land in ye County's of Richmond and Westmoreland." Witnessed by Jn. Grayson and Cary Keble. Recorded in Richmond County Court March 3, 1714. Attested by M[armaduke] Beckwith, Clerk.

Indenture of release for 840 acres of land adjoining property of Colonel Lloyd, dec'd., George Brown, Richard Sutten, William Robinson, and Colonel Pierce. [17]

1713 Oct. 15. SHARSHALL GRASTY to ROBERT CARTER. DS. 1 p. Witnessed by J. W. Grayson and William Ranken. Seal intact.

Bond for performance of covenant, signed by Sharshall Grasty, in sale of 840 acres of land in Richmond and Westmoreland Counties to Robert Carter. [18]

1714 Apr. 28. JOHN COPPRIDGE, Surveyor of Counties of Northampton and Lancaster. ADS. 1 p.

Survey map and description of three parcels of land in Richmond County owned by Daniel McCarty of Westmoreland County and purchased by him from John Rice and Walter Pavey. (L. C. later bought part of this land from Daniel McCarty; see September 4, 1738.) [19]

1714 Aug. 2. JAMES ALDERSON, Deputy Clerk of Essex County, to DANIEL McCARTY. ALS. 1 p.

Reports failure to find record of sale of the other half of tract sold by William Underwood to [ ] Mead, or of the will of Walter Pavey, "having searched from 1656, the beginning of the County records, to 1672." Observes that the will may have been burned in William Colston's house when he had possession of the records. [20]

1714 Aug. 13. WEBLEY PAVEY to DANIEL McCARTY. DS. 2 pp. Witnessed by John Tarpley, Jr., Allan Hunter, Will Cruckshanke, James Collett. Recorded in Richmond County Court September 1, 1714. Attested by Thomas Dickenson, Deputy Clerk. Seal intact.

Indenture of lease. Pavey acknowledges receipt of five shillings and agrees to lease 350 acres of land to McCarty. (See January 4, 1714-15; August 2, 1714; September 4, 1738.)   [21]

1714 Aug. 31. WEBLEY PAVEY to DANIEL McCARTY. DS. 2 pp. Witnessed by John Tarpley, Allan Hunter, Will Cruckshanke, and [   ]. Recorded in Richmond County Court September 1, 1714. Attested by Tho. Dickenson, Deputy Clerk.

Indenture of sale. Pavey acknowledges receipt of £200 in consideration of sale of 350 acres of land in Richmond County. (This is a part of the land purchased by L.C. from Daniel McCarty, September 4, 1738.)   [22]

1714 Nov. 30. BENJAMIN HINDS and MARY HINDS, his wife, to DANIEL McCARTY. DS. 2 pp. Witnessed by Samuel Peachey, Darby Driskale, and Mary Harris. Docketed. Recorded in Richmond County Court February 2, 1714-15. Attested by M[armaduke] Beckwith, Clerk.

Indenture of sale. Benjamin and Mary Hinds, daughter of Thomas Fuller, in consideration of 8,000 pounds of tobacco, agree to sell to Daniel McCarty 100 acres of land in Richmond County. (This land later purchased by L.C. from Daniel McCarty; see September 1, 1683 and September 4, 1738.) [23]

1714-15 Jan. 4. WEBLEY PAVEY to DANIEL McCARTY. DS. 2 pp. Acknowledged in Richmond County Court February 2, 1714-15. Attested by M[armaduke] Beckwith, Clerk. Seal intact.

Indenture of release. Webley Pavey, for consideration of 2,000 pounds of tobacco, releases deed to 100 acres of land in Mangorick Creek in Richmond County. Tract originally held by Walter and Mary Pavey, and sold to Thomas Fuller, father of Mary Hinds, who conveyed title to Daniel McCarty. (See September 4, 1783.)   [24]

1715 Mar. 31. JOHN MINOR, of Westmoreland County, to JOHN CHAMPE, of Richmond County. DS. 2 pp. Witnessed by John Moulton, Thomas Bashlar, and William Moulton. Acknowledged and recorded in Westmoreland County Court April 27, 1715. Attested by Thomas Sorrell, Deputy Clerk.

Indenture of release. Conveys to John Champe 100 acres of land in Westmoreland County for 4,000 pounds of tobacco. (See July 20, 1732 and September 4, 1738.) [25]

1723 Nov. 14-15. JOHN WARNER for DANIEL McCARTY. AD. 1 p. Survey of "Green's Land" (lying southeast of Daniel McCarty's holding). Also survey map and legend indicating Daniel McCarty's holdings on the Rappahannock River and Brushwood Creek.   [26]

1727 Oct. 31. MARMADUKE BECKWITH, of Richmond County, to RICHARD DOGGITT and ANN, his wife. ADS. 1 p. Witnessed by Thomas Gearing. Acknowledged and recorded in Richmond County Court November 1, 1727. Attested by M[armaduke] Beckwith, Clerk.

Indenture of lease. For consideration of 5 shillings, Beckwith leases to Doggitt a parcel of land of 70 acres for one year. (This tract purchased by L.C. from Marmaduke Beckwith; see February 28, 1734.) [27]

1731 May 8. JOHN WARNER, Surveyor, King George County. ADS. 1 p.
Map and description of a tract of 895 acres of land on south side of the "Sherrando" (Shenandoah) River in Prince William County and belonging to Landon Carter. [28]

ca. 1731. A PLAT OF LAND HELD BY COL. WM. LLOYD ON MANGORICK AND THE FORK. D. 1 p. Docketed by L.C.
Indicates the boundaries of the land sold by William Fauntleroy to Col. William Lloyd, according to a survey made February 27, 1683 by William Moseley, and the land bought by William Lloyd from Walter Pavey. (See February 27, 1683-84 and January 4, 1714-15.) [29]

1732 July 20. JOHN CHAMPE and JOHN CHAMPE, JR., both of King George County, to EDWARD BARRADALL of the same county. DS. 1 p. Witnessed by Baldwin Mathews, John Horelle, Phillip Sanders, and Thomas Gearing. Docketed.
"Bond for performance of covenants." Amount of bond, £370, as proof of intent to keep covenants agreed upon. (See March 31, 1715; May 28, 1733; and August 5, 1735.) [30]

1733 May 28. ED[WARD] BARRADALL of Westmoreland County, to L.C. of Lancaster County. DS.

1 p. Witnessed by Catsby Corke and Tho. Gearing. Acknowledged and recorded in Westmoreland County Court June 29, 1733. Attested by G. Turberville, Clerk, and in Richmond County Court, attested by M[armaduke] Beckwith, Clerk. Docketed.
Indenture of lease. For five shillings, Barradall agrees to lease to L.C. a tract of 624 acres of land in Westmoreland County for one year. (See March 31, 1715; July 20, 1732; and August 5, 1735.) [31]

1733 May 29. EDWARD BARRADALL to L.C. DS. 2 pp. Witnessed by Catsby Corke and Thomas Gearing. Acknowledged and recorded in Westmoreland County Court June 4, 1733. Attested by G. Turberville, Clerk, and in Richmond County Court June 5, 1733, attested by M[armaduke] Beckwith. Docketed.
Indenture of release. Barradall acknowledges receipt of £200 and releases to L.C. title to a tract of 624 acres of land in Westmoreland County. (This became an important part of L.C.'s productive estate.) [32]

1734-35 Jan. 2. EDWARD ATHAWES, agent, bought of MARTHA WILLIAMS, London, for ROBERT CARTER, JR.'S ESTATE. D. 1 p. Docketed by L.C.
"Shop note." List of millinery amounting to £24.14.7. [33]

1734-35 Feb. 28. MARMADUKE BECKWITH to L.C. ADS. 2 pp. Docketed. Witnessed by Gilbert Hamilton, Henry Lee, and Thomas Barber. Acknowledged and recorded in Richmond County

Court. Attested by M[armaduke] Beckwith, Clerk.

Bond for £80 sterling for performance of covenants. [34]

1735. LAND TITLE PAPERS. 7 items. D.

Five of the items are arguments in defense of the title to part of L.C.'s Mangorick property. Details of the arguments trace the possession of the land through the hands of Col. William Lloyd, Thomas Fuller, Walter Pavey, Webley Pavey, Richard Webley, Richard Loes and John Rice, and William Underwood.

Also two plats of the tract, together with the description of the boundaries. [35]

1735-36 Jan. 20. SURVEY of tract of land on Rappahannock River by L.C., Col. John Tayloe, William Deggar, Maj. William Fauntleroy, and others. AD. 2 pp.

A survey of L.C.'s "Landsdowne" property in Richmond County. [36]

1735 Aug. 5. EDWARD BARRADALL to L.C. DS. 1 p. Docketed. Witnessed by Thomas Gearing and M[armaduke] Beckwith. Acknowledged and recorded in Richmond County Court August 5, 1735. Attested by M[armaduke] Beckwith, Clerk.

Bond for £80 for performance of covenants. [37]

1736 Dec. 20. EDWARD ATHAWES to JOHN and CHARLES CARTER. ALS. 2 pp. End.

London agent of "Nomini" estate reports action on accounts as requested. Makes pointed complaint about quality of tobacco shipped from "Nomini," and of his difficulties in selling the inferior grade. [38]

1736 Dec. 31. EDWARD ATHAWES to JOHN, CHARLES, and LANDON CARTER. ALS. 2 pp.

Reports making purchases as ordered. Repeats complaint about quality of tobacco shipped from "Nomini." (These three brothers were the trustees of the estate of the young Robert Carter, their nephew.) [39]

1736-37 Mar. 10. EDWARD ATHAWES to JOHN and CHARLES CARTER. ALS. 1 p. End.

Reports sale of 97 hhd. of tobacco for £707.5. Again complains of quality of tobacco. He suggests that it had been poorly handled and requests that the overseer be admonished. [40]

1738 June 30. DANIEL McCARTY to L.C. DS. 1 p. Attested by George Lee. Docketed.

Acknowledges receipt of £300 purchase money for Mangorick land. (This was an important section of the "Sabine Hall" estate.) [41]

1738 July 15. CHARLES CARTER of "Cleve," to L.C. [his brother]. ALS. 1 p.

Requests loan of £20. Comments on serious shortage of money in his area. [42]

1738 Aug. 7. DANIEL McCARTY to L.C. ALS. 1 p. End.

Reports progress in projected land sales. Requests that L.C. forward about £40. Postscript reads:

"We are just starving for want of bread, if you can help us pray do." [43]

1738 Sept. 4. DENNIS McCARTY, of Prince William, and DANIEL McCARTY, of Westmoreland, to L.C. DS. 2 pp. Docketed. Witnessed by R[ ] Corbin, Richard Barnes, and Samuel Eskridge. Acknowledged and recorded in Richmond County Court September 4, 1738. Attested by M[armaduke] Beckwith, Clerk. Seals intact.

Bond for £1200 for performance of covenants. [44]

1738 Sept. 4. DENNIS and SARAH McCARTY, of Prince William, and DANIEL McCARTY to L.C. DS. 4 pp. Docketed. Deed witnessed by R[ ] Corbin, Richard Barnes, and Samuel Eskridge. Acknowledged and recorded in Richmond County Court September 4, 1738. Attested by M[armaduke] Beckwith, Clerk. [In Deed Book No. 9, 1738, Richmond County Court.]

Indenture of sale. The McCartys acknowledge receipt of £500 in consideration of sale of tract of land "lying on the northside of the Rappahannock River in the County of Richmond, and lying between a rise in the creeks called M[ ], Bryars Creek, Mangorick Creek, and Brushwood Creek and said riverside which said lands are part of a patent granted to William Underwood, dec'd. and by sundry conveyances into the possession of Richard Webley, dec'd., and from him descended to Mary his daughter and heiress afterwards the wife of Walter Pavey, dec'd. and by sundry other conveyances from this Walter and

Mary his wife and Webley Pavey son and heir of the said Mary. [ ] came into the actual possession of Daniel McCarty late of Westmoreland County, dec'd. father of the [Dennis and] Daniel parties hereto by his last will and testament...." (This is the deed to an important section of the "Sabine Hall" estate; see March 10, 1664; January 3, 1680-81; February 27, 1683-84; January 21, 1683; October 6, 1693; January 4, 1714-15; November 30, 1714; March 31, 1715; June 30, 1738.)

Also a commission signed by M[armaduke] Beckwith, Clerk, directing Captain Thomas Wright Belfield and Mr. Gilbert Hamilton, Trustees of Richmond County, to proceed to contact Sarah McCarty and obtain her acknowledgement of certain deed of sale between Dennis and Sarah McCarty and L.C. [45]

1738 Nov. DENNIS McCARTY to "Landown Carter, Esq., at Wm Burgh." ADS. 1 p. Witnessed by Marv. Lawson, Jn. Therman, and A. Mercer. Attested by Wm. Payne.

Names and values of four slaves annexed to 1,000 acre tract sold by Dennis McCarty to L.C. (See September 4, 1738.) [46]

1738 Dec. 28. WM. LOVEY, London, to L.C. ALS. 1 p. End.

Reports receipt of shipment of tobacco, damaged in transport. [47]

1738 Nov. 14. MAP AND SURVEY by THOMAS BARBER, Surveyor for Richmond County. ADS. 1 p. Docketed.

Map and description of 375 acre

tract known as the "Riverside Field" sold to L.C. by Dennis McCarty. (This tract became a part of the "Sabine Hall" estate.) [48]

[*ca.* 1738.] Two MEMORANDA listing ownership of [the William] Underwood patent. D. 3 pp. Docketed.

One lists chronology of ownership from William Underwood's patent of 1650 to purchase by Dennis McCarty. Verso of this bears plat and survey of the tract.

The other lists patents granted to Captain Moore Fauntleroy "between the years 1643 and 1651." [49]

1739 Apr. 23. DENNIS McCARTY to L.C. D. 1 p. Docketed. Attested by J. W. Belfield and Gilbert Hamilton.

Fragment of deed. Dennis McCarty acknowledges receipt of £188 in consideration of sale of 425-acre tract in Richmond County. (This was part of a tract patented to William Underwood in 1650 and later purchased by L.C.) [50]

1739 June 14. JOHN CARTER, Williamsburg, to L.C. ALS. 1 p. End.

Reports rumored attempt by an unnamed party to gain possession of "Nomini" estate. [51]

1739 July 11. JOHN CARTER, "Shirley," to L.C., "Landsdowne." ALS. 2 pp. End.

John Carter, L.C.'s older brother, reports arrival of slave ship from Gold Coast. Also describes quality and price of a group of slaves that he had bought for L.C. and which he was sending to him. [52]

1739-40 Mar. 3. JOHN CARTER, "Shirley," to L.C., "Landsdowne." 1 p. End.

Letter of condolence on the death of Elizabeth Wormeley Carter, L.C.'s wife. Also mentions plans for spring journey, and matter of business of buying corn. [53]

1741 Jan. 2. Copy of WILL of GEORGE CARTER of the Middle Temple, London. D. 2 pp. Docketed. Attested by Robert Livesey, Thomas Gamull, and John Evans.

George Carter, younger brother of L.C., bequeaths to his brothers the slaves and utensils then on the lands which they would inherit through him from the will of their father, Robert Carter. Provides that the brothers were to receive no further part of his real or personal property. (In his will Robert Carter bequeathed thousands of acres of land to Landon and George Carter jointly, with the provision that, should one die without male heir, the other should come into possession of the share of the deceased.) [54]

1741 May. L.C. AD. 2 pp.

Detailed description of a plant which he picked on the summit of a hill at "Sabine Hall." [55]

1741 Nov. 2. EDWARD SPENCER, Orange County, to L.C. DS. 2 pp. Docketed. Acknowledged and recorded in Richmond County Court. Attested by M[armaduke] Beckwith, Clerk.

Indenture of sale. Acknowledges receipt of £65 for tract of land in Lunenburg Parish in Richmond County. Tract "bounded by and adjoining the lands of Benjamin

Rust, William Gore, and the land formerly belonging to Thadeus McCarty, dec'd. and now to the said Landon Carter." [56]

1746 July 7. JOHN and MARY WHITE, of King George County, to BENJAMIN RUST. D. 3 pp. Docketed. Witnessed by Richard Corey, Minthon Morgan, John Paterson, Metcalfe Rust, and Margarette Smith. Acknowledged and recorded in the Richmond County Court July 7, 1746. Attested by M[armaduke] Beckwith. Certified by Leroy Peachey.

Copy of indenture of release. Acknowledges receipt of £100 for release of 100 acres of land to Benjamin Rust for his lifetime and that of his son, Richard. Tract lay on Bryar Creek adjoining the land of L.C. (L.C. later purchased this land from Benjamin Rust.) [57]

1747 May 6. CHARLES CARTER, "Curles," to L.C. ALS. 1 p. End.

Reports his inability to collect back rent at "Westover." (The letter does not contain the names of the parties involved.) [58]

1750 Sept. 15. SURVEY by WILLIAM GARLAND for L.C. ADS. 1 p. Docketed. Witnessed by Gilbert Hamilton and John Tayloe. Recorded in Richmond County Court. Attested by Trav[ers] Tarpley, Deputy Clerk.

Survey of 100-acre tract lying between that of L.C. and that of Benjamin Rust. [59]

1752 Nov. 6. JOHN and ANN WHITE, of Orange County, to BENJAMIN RUST. D. 4 pp. Certified by Leroy Peachey, Clerk. Acknowledged and recorded in Richmond County Court, November 6, 1752. Attested by T[ravers] Tarpley, Deputy Clerk.

Indenture of release. Acknowledges receipt of £70 for sale of 200 acres in Richmond County inherited by Ann White from her great-grandmother, Ann Branham. (Tract later purchased by L.C.) [60]

1753 Oct. 12. [L.C.] to "THE GENTLEMEN PLANTERS OF VIRGINIA." AL. 3 pp. End.

Draft of humorous letter signed "Londonensis," fictitious London merchant bidding for business among Virginia planters. A satire on the questionable business practices of the merchants of the day. [61]

1754 Feb. 19. BENJAMIN RUST, of Richmond County. D. 3 pp. Copy attested by Leroy Peachey, Clerk. Witnessed by Henry Miskell, John Lowry, William Barber, and Winnifred Morgan.

Will of Benjamin Rust, former owner of part of "Sabine Hall" estate. [62]

1754 July 2. WILLIAM GARLAND, Surveyor, for JOHN HARFORD. ADS. 1 p. Docketed by L.C.

Survey and map of 60-acre tract owned by Harford and bought by L.C. as part of "Sabine Hall" estate. [63]

1755 Oct. 23. WILLIAM GARLAND to L.C. ADS. 2 pp. Witnessed by Francis Chrestien.

Bond for £500 for conveyance of mill and land bought by L.C. from William Garland's father. This land and water mill adjoined "Sabine Hall," and had been bought for £20 and a tract of land lying between L.C.'s property and that of William Garland, Sr.   [64]

1758 Apr. 26. CHARLES CARTER, "Cleve," to L.C. ALS. 1 p. End.
     Writes that he had found a young woman of 24 years whom he planned to marry to take the place of his deceased wife.   [65]

1759 July 10. [L.C.] AD. 1 p. Docketed.
     Survey and map of "Fork Land" tract of "Sabine Hall." This tract contains 277 acres lying along boundary between the property of L.C. and the John Tayloe estate.   [66]

1760 Apr. 10. G[EORGE] W[ILLIAM] FAIRFAX to L.C. ALS. 1 p. End. and D. 1 p. Docketed.
     As agent for the Proprietor, Lord Fairfax, he requests that L.C. pay balance on quit rent account. Includes a record of the account, which indicated a balance of £433.5.9 for the years 1743 to 1759 on 44,294 acres of land.
     On verso is comment by L.C., "a most erroneous account, no credit given for four years and too much land charged."   [67]

1761 Jan. 20. JOSEPH ROYLE, Williamsburg, to L.C. ALS. 1 p. End.
     Editor of *Virginia Gazette* regrets that he would not be able to publish in entirety a letter L.C. had written to "Col. P.T.," because it would have filled the entire paper.   [68]

1762 Apr. 12. JOHN TAYLOE, Williamsburg, to L.C. ALS. 4 pp. End.
     Writing at the request of Governor Francis Fauquier, John Tay-

loe asks that L.C. give the Governor the right to reprieve Mr. Rust's servant Harry on condition that the latter "be removed a safe distance from the area." (The offense was not mentioned.)   [69]

1762 June 22. ALEXANDER PURDIE, Williamsburg, to L.C. ALS. 1 p. End.
     Alexander Purdie, writing in the absence of Joseph Royle, acknowledges receipt of L.C.'s letter for publication and states that he has had a proof struck and is forwarding it to "Sabine Hall" for certain inspection.   [70]

1762 July 27. CHARLES CARTER, JR., "Cleve," to L.C. ALS. 1 p. End.
     Requests that L.C. come to "Cleve" to be with Charles Carter, Sr., who was seriously ill and possibly dying. (Col. Charles Carter recovered from this illness and lived for two more years.)   [71]

1762 Sept. 17. JOHN TAYLOE, "Mount Airy," to L.C. ALS. 1 p. End.
     Requests to borrow £400 for one month. Mentions business dealings with a merchant in Boston.   [72]

1762 Oct. 16. JOHN TAYLOE, Williamsburg, to L.C. ALS. 1 p. End.
     John Tayloe, friend and neighbor, informs L.C. that a Rev. William Townsend was preparing to sue L.C. for defamation as a result of a comment L.C. had made in one of his writings. Also requests that L.C. ride over to "Mount Airy" and give the overseer his suggestions as to mending the fences.   [73]

1763 Jan. 4. CHARLES CARTER, SR., "Cleve," to L.C. ALS. 2 pp. and wrapper. End.

Indicates surprise at the news of the proposed marriage of L.C.'s daughter, Marie Carter, to Robert Beverley of "Blandfield." Doubts the fitness of the young man unless certain matters could be clarified, such as his frequent need of money and the report that he had almost killed one Thomas Knap in a duel with pistols. [74]

1763 Feb. 1 and 2. "MINUTES OF THE PROCEEDINGS OF THE LORDS COMMISSIONERS FOR TRADE AND PLANTATIONS." D. 3 pp. Docketed by L.C. Certified by J. Pownall.

Copy of official proceedings dealing with complaints by the merchants of London about the large amounts of money being printed in the Colony of Virginia, and also of the conduct of the Legislature of that Colony. Resolution passed on the second day observes "the creating and issuing of paper bills of credit to be injurious to the commerce of Great Britain and inconsistent with interests of the Crown and to be stopped immediately." (L.C., as a member of the House of Burgesses, was directly concerned with this matter.) [75]

1763 July 5. EDWARD MONTAGUE, London, to ARTHUR LEE. ALS. 4 pp. End.

Edward Montague, agent in England for the Assembly of Virginia, had attended the February 1 and 2 meeting of the Board of Trade. In this letter he recounts the background and action of the meeting. (An excellent description of the attitude of the Government toward the colonies; see February 1 and 2, 1763.) [76]

1763 Feb. 6. NELSON BERKELEY, ["Airwell," Hanover County], to L.C. ALS. 2 pp. End.

Husband of L.C.'s daughter, Elizabeth, discusses family affairs, health, etc. Alludes to the marriage of L.C.'s daughter, Marie, to Robert Beverley. [77]

1763 Apr. 15. RICHARD CORBIN, Williamsburg, to L.C. ALS. 1 p. End.

Reports on the progress of the business of the court in Williamsburg. [78]

1763 May 13. WILLIAM FITZHUGH, "Marmion," to L.C. ALS. 2 pp. End.

Expresses regret that L.C. was not going to the Assembly "when called on so important matters." Feels that traveling and the variety of company would be a relief from the "disorders" that were affecting L.C. [79]

1763 May 26. THOMAS NELSON, Williamsburg, to L.C. ALS. 2 pp. End.

Expresses pleasure that L.C. has undertaken to cultivate vines, and encourages him to pursue his intention to make wine. He held that such a project would be profitable not only to "the adventurer but to the country as well." (L.C. was interested in increasing the variety of crops in the area.) [80]

1763. CHARLES CARTER, "Cleve," to L.C. ALS. 2 pp. End.

Reports favorable comment

"Col. Thornton" had made to Col. Tayloe concerning letter L.C. had written for publication in answer to that of Peter Wyches. Announces that his daughter, Judith, "by her own unalterable determination married on Tuesday last." P.S. "I can spare you some cash if you come up."   [81]

1763 Aug. PETER WYCHES to COL. CHARLES CARTER and GOVERNOR [FRANCIS] FAUQUIER. L. 2 pp. End. by L.C.
Extracts of letter concerning the growing of grapes in the colonies, and comments on the desirability of raising bees in Virginia. Letter was forwarded to L.C. by his brother, Charles Carter.   [82]

1763 Sept. 8. WILLIAM BROCKENBROUGH to L.C. ALS. 1 p. End.
A neighbor of L.C. regrets the action taken by L.C. in killing his neighbor's hogs before anything could be done to prevent them from wandering into L.C.'s land, and asks that, if any more should trespass, L.C. drive them back home without killing them.   [83]

1764 Jan. 1. LANDON CARTER, JR., of Pittsylvania, to L.C. ALS. 1 p. End.
L.C.'s son reports that he was returning a runaway slave, Sammy, to L.C. by his overseer, Joseph Florance. Requests that L.C. send coffee and garden seeds. Announces intention of sending part of his tobacco crop to Falmouth. Reports that his children had been ill, and that he had been forced to practice on them himself

and registers apprehension that he would harm them.   [84]

1764 Jan. 1. CHARLES CARTER of "Corotoman," to L.C. ALS. 1 p. End.
New Year's greeting from L.C.'s brother: "God preserve your life, your health, your limbs, your spirits, and your friendships."   [85]

1764 Jan. 21. ROBERT CARTER, Williamsburg, to L.C. ALS. 2 pp. End.
Robert Carter sends greetings from Williamsburg and reports shortage of provisions in the town. Reports that during the previous week he had attended for the first time a meeting of the Committee of Correspondence in which had been read a letter from the Agent, Edward Montague, reporting the repeal of the last "Insolent" Act, and of the further legislation of Parliament.   [86]

1764 Jan. 24. RICHARD CORBIN, Laneville, to L.C. ALS. 1 p. End.
Reports receipt of orders amounting to £116.18.10. Reports that the Assembly had passed an act to pay the militia for service against the Indians the previous summer out of funds voted by Parliament.   [87]

1764 Feb. 15. NELSON BERKELEY, Hanover, to L.C. ALS. 1 p. End.
Apologizes for not being able to wait upon the father-in-law as promised, because of illness of his daughter.   [88]

1764 Mar. 9. RALPH WORMELEY, "Rosegill," to L.C. ALS. 1 p. End.
Replies to L.C.'s request for the papers relating to the land

L.C. had purchased from Ralph Wormeley's brother. Reports that Ralph Wormeley, Jr. might get the post of Collector of the Colony. [89]

1764 Apr. 10. NELSON BERKELEY to L.C. ALS. 1 p. End.
Announces the birth of a son on March 21 and promises to bring his wife to visit her parents as soon as she is able to travel. [90]

1764 Apr. 26. JOHN TAYLOE, Williamsburg, to L.C. ALS. 2 pp. End.
Reports that the Governor had been highly pleased at the letter which L.C. had written to the merchants of England. [91]

1764 May 9. ROBERT CARTER NICHOLAS, Williamsburg, to L.C. ALS. 2 pp. End.
L.C.'s nephew reports the progress of affairs in the court in Williamsburg. [92]

1764 Nov. REV. ISAAC W. GIBERNE, "Sabine Hall," to L.C. at Williamsburg. ALS. 4 pp. End.
(Isaac Giberne was the Rector of Lunenburg Parish and a close friend of L.C.) Discusses news received from England, of the talk of war with France and Spain, and of the pensioning of Lords Sandwich and Halifax. Reports receipt of deputation from John, Duke of Argyle, to be the latter's chaplain. Requests that L.C. purchase for him a walking stick, and that he pay a bill of 29 shillings to Joseph Royle, editor of the *Virginia Gazette*. [93]

1764 Nov. 16. ROBERT WORMELEY CARTER, "Sabine Hall," to L.C., Williamsburg. ALS. 3 pp. End.
The oldest son of L.C. reports the events of three days of supervising the work at "Sabine Hall." Comments on the threshing of wheat, the storing of corn, and the problem of securing sufficient pork "as the plantation is overrun with sows." Reports the arrival of a shipment of clothes from England, observing that "your prints are pretty, and your clothes vastly genteel." [94]

ca. 1765. "A CASE STATED AS TO THE RIGHT OF ACTION IN THE PLAINTIFF." D. 4 pp.
Sets forth arguments against the claim by Charles Carter, Jr. on the executors of Charles Carter, Sr., John and Landon Carter. Supported by a copy of the agreement between Charles, Jr. and Charles Carter, Sr. in which the former purportedly accepted a large gift of land and slaves from the father (June 3, 1762) and in exchange discharged the father of any further demand on that account.
(An interesting case involving primogeniture, in this instance the problem being compounded by the father's having granted lands to his son and then purchasing them from him.) [95]

1765 Feb. 15. PRESLEY THORNTON to L.C. ALS. 2 pp. End.
Friendly letter dealing mainly with the health of L.C. and the writer. [96]

1765 Mar. 17. NELSON BERKELEY to L.C. ALS. 2 pp. End.
Comments on the "attack" made on L.C. at Williamsburg. He again assures L.C. of his respect and

gratitude. (L.C. did not mention the incident in his own writings.) [97]

1765 Apr. 8. NELSON BERKELEY to L.C. ALS. 1 p. End.

Having been informed that all at "Sabine Hall" were ill, Berkeley sends a messenger to inquire about the health of the family. [98]

1765 May 20. CHARLES CARTER, of "Corotoman," from Williamsburg, to L.C. ALS. 1 p. End.

Urges L.C. to attend a called meeting of the Assembly to discuss ways and means of extricating the colony "out of its present deplorable circumstances." Comments on the proposal to seek the establishment of a Loan Office of some £100,000 to be borrowed from England. [99]

1765 June. JUDITH BANKS, "Cleve," to L.C. ALS. 2 pp. End.

(Judith Banks was the sister of Charles Carter's first wife and in charge of domestic affairs at "Cleve" following his death in 1764.) Requests that L.C. send money with which she could buy clothes for the children and the negroes. Comments on "the trouble your brother's affairs must give all that were concerned." [100]

1765 June 25. WILL[IAM] CHURCHILL, "Wilton," to L.C. ALS. 1 p.

Requests that L.C. pay the £300 owed by the estate of the late Col. Charles Carter. (L.C. was one of the executors of his brother's estate.) [101]

1765 July 5. JOHN WOODBRIDGE, Richmond County, to "THE FREEHOLDERS OF RICH-MOND COUNTY." ALS. 1 p. End.

John Woodbridge, long-time Burgess from Richmond County, announces his decision not to seek re-election to the Assembly. (L.C. had been the associate of John Woodbridge in the Assembly for the previous twelve years.) [102]

1765 July 13. LANDON CARTER, "Cleve," to L.C. ALS. 1 p. End.

The son of Charles Carter informs his uncle that he was "in great want of clothes." Also an undated letter containing an account of his life at school. (As one of the executors of the estate of Charles Carter, L.C. made financial provisions for the children.) [103]

1765 Nov. 4. L.C. to JONAS GREENE. AL. 2 pp. End: "Copy to Jonas Greene, November 4, 1765."

Message requests that Jonas Greene return to L.C. a letter written for publication remonstrating against the Acts of Parliament. Requests that the letter not be sent by post, in order to avoid the purchase of stamps. In the letter L.C. denounces the Stamp Act and taxation by other than popular representatives. [104]

1765 Nov. 30. [L.C.] to Mr. [ ] in England. AL. 24 pp.

A draft of a letter from "an inhabitant of North America" in which L.C. gave a "little consideration" to an article written by a William Pym and published in the "Public Ledger" on August 25, 1765. William Pym's article attempted to set forth the British view on the right of Parliament to tax the colonies. L.C.'s letter presents a detailed account of the colonists' view on the subject. [105]

1765 Dec. 27. ROBERT CARTER, Williamsburg, to L.C. ALS. 1 p. End.

Robert Carter, of "Nomini Hall," requests his uncle to give him an account of the genealogy of the Carter family. He requests particularly the details of the European roots and relationships of the family. [106]

[1766] JOHN TAYLOE, ["Mount Airy"], to L.C. ALS. 1 p. End.

Requests that L.C. dine with him in order to meet and discuss the colonial issue with an agent sent to America by Lord Shelburne, currently Foreign Minister and Acting Prime Minister, to inquire into the dispute. In the endorsement L.C. comments on the bad weather and the interview. [107]

1766 Jan. 27. ROBERT CARTER NICHOLAS, Williamsburg, to L.C. ALS. 1 p. End.

L.C.'s nephew introduces Robert Miller, Public Printer, who desired the support of L.C. in some project heartily approved by Robert Carter Nicholas. [108]

1766 Feb. 10. CHARLES CARTER, "of the Park," to his uncle, L.C. ALS. 1 p. End.

Requests that L.C. furnish him with a buck rabbit and some Lucerne seed. Reports on disturbances in northern Virginia over the Stamp Act. [109]

1766 Mar. A copy of the pamphlet "MUSEUM RUSTICUM" for March 1766. 40 pp.

On the margin L.C. made numerous notes. Some of these comments are critical and some are memoranda of his intent to experiment with some of the proposals. [110]

1766 Mar. 22. JUDITH BANKS, "Cleve," to L.C. ALS. 1 p. End.

Expresses gratitude for all that L.C. had done for the orphaned children of his brother, and solicits patience with the tempers of the children. "P.S.: the wheat is so full of weavels its impossible to eat it, we live entirely on corn bread." [111]

1766 Aug. 20. THOMAS BRYAN MARTIN to L.C. ALS. 1 p. End.

The agent for Lord Fairfax notifies L.C. that the proprietor had ordered collectors to re-enter the lands assigned to the estate of the late George Carter as a result of unpaid quit rents. He also requests settlement of the quit rent account of the late Col. Charles Carter, and asks that L.C. instruct his sons to appear at "Greenway Court" to attempt to satisfy the accounts. (L.C. was an executor of the estates of his two brothers.) [112]

1766 Nov. 29. JOHN and ELIZABETH BEALE, Richmond County, to JOHN TAYLOE, LANDON CARTER, and WILLIAM FAUNTLEROY. DS. 2 pp. Docketed. Witnessed by William Beale, Richard Parkey, Robert Deggs, and John Beale, Jr. Acknowledged and recorded in Richmond County Court December 1, 1766. Attested by Leroy Peachey, Deputy Clerk.

Indenture of release. For £650,

money of Virginia, releases to the vestrymen of Lunenburg Parish a tract of 400 acres of land to be added to the parish glebe, "except a small part to be laid off for a poor house."   [113]

1767 Mar. 20. JOHN TAYLOE, Williamsburg, to ROBERT WORMELEY CARTER, "Sabine Hall." ALS. 2 pp. End.

Outlines the details of the proposed sale of the "Landsdowne" plantation by Robert Wormeley Carter, who had been given this property by his father.   [114]

[1768] "TO THE MEMBERS OF THE LATE HOUSE OF REPRESENTATIVES OF MASSACHUSETTS BAY." AL. 4 pp.

A draft of a circular letter written "by a Virginian" in L.C.'s hand. Expresses sympathetic concern for the plight of Massachusetts Bay Colony and extends encouragement to its leaders. (The occasion was the disbanding in 1768 of the House of Representatives after it had refused to rescind a circular letter concerning the dispute with Parliament in the matter of taxation.)   [115]

1768 Jan. 6. REV. ISAAC W. GIBERNE, "Belle-Ville," to L.C. ALS. 1 p. End.

The rector of the parish apologizes for the bad manners of his wife in not accepting an invitation to "Sabine Hall."   [116]

1768 Feb. 6. Rev. ISAAC W. GIBERNE, "Belle-Ville," to L.C. ALS. 1 p. End.

The rector expresses his willingness to buy beef from L.C. At the end of the letter he comments on trip to Westmoreland County.   [117]

1768 May 21. REV. ISAAC W. GIBERNE, "Belle-Ville," to L.C. ALS. 1 p. End.

In this letter, the rector reports his disappointment at not receiving the appointment from the Bishop of London to a post to which he aspired and for which L.C. and the Governor of the Colony had interceded in vain.   [118]

1768 June 10. RALPH WORMELEY, JR., "Rosegill," to L.C. ALS. 3 pp. End.

Young Ralph Wormeley expresses surprise at the rumor that he was to be appointed Deputy Secretary of the Colony, and further expresses bitter doubt that any such good fortune could come to him. (Ralph Wormeley, Jr. was a nephew of L.C.'s first wife.)   [119]

1768 July 8. REV. ISAAC W. GIBERNE, "Belle-Ville," to L.C. ALS. 1 p. End.

The letter concerns minor business affairs. The rector closes the letter with the casual comment that the ague which had bothered him was disappearing, and that the matter which had made his condition worse was the elopement of his wife, "who, I am credibly informed, keeps company every night with some strolling players."   [120]

1768 July 12. THOMAS BRYAN MARTIN to L.C. ADS. 1 p. Docketed.

A bill for quit rents due Lord Fairfax on 44,294 acres of land for the years 1760 to 1767 plus a balance of £102.19.10 due as of 1760. Total bill was £457.6.10. (According to the records, this account was never settled.) [121]

1768 Aug. 28. REV. ISAAC W. GIBERNE, "Belle-Ville," to L.C. ALS. 1 p. End.

Requests to "beg, borrow, or buy a couple or three bushels of barley for seed." The rector planned on growing his own grain for making beverages. [122]

1768 [Nov.] A copy of a VERSE concerning L.C. sent to Col. Tayloe a little before the Richmond election of 1768, and "THE ANSWER" by L.C.

A satirical eulogy of L.C. evidently written by a political enemy; Carter's reply is a clever piece of verse expressing his attitude toward public service and private honor. [123]

1768 Nov. 1. [L.C.] to NORBORNE BERKELEY, LORD BOTETOURT, Governor of Virginia. AL. 2 pp. End: "Rough copy of letter to His Excellency, Lord Botetourt."

L.C. apologizes for not waiting upon the new Governor upon his arrival in the colony, and expresses his best wishes for a good administration. In this letter L.C. referred to himself as Lieutenant of Richmond County, a position which he held under the administrations of William Gooch, Robert Dinwiddie, and Francis Fauquier, the Lieutenant Governors who preceded Governor Botetourt as administrators of the colony. [124]

1768 Nov. 5. REBECCA TAYLOE to L.C. 1 p. End.

The wife of John Tayloe thanks L.C. for a fine breast of venison, but states certainly that it had been shot on Tayloe property. In his endorsement L.C. alludes to Rebecca Tayloe's note as a "curious return for the venison," but does not deny the accusation.

[125]

1768 Nov. 26. REV. ISAAC W. GIBERNE, "Belle-Ville," to L.C. ALS. 2 pp. End.

The rector attempts to explain Rebecca Tayloe's curious note about the venison. Chides L.C. for permitting his taste for venison to threaten to destroy neighborliness, and comments on the efforts of John and Rebecca Tayloe to conserve the deer in the area. [126]

1769 May 14. L.C. to [   ]. AL. 2 pp.

This is a draft of a letter written to an old friend, cautioning him not to be deluded by the efforts of Parliament to compliment Virginia while continuing to persecute the other colonies. L.C. refers to Virginia as the first colony to cry out against tyranny and holds that the actions of the other colonies were steps of boldness along the path laid by Virginia. L.C. felt that Parliament was attempting to punish the followers while complimenting the principal. He warns that, even if the existing restrictions were lifted, more would come. [127]

1769 Dec. 8. PETER PELHAM, Williamsburg, to L.C. ALS. 1 p. End.

Peter Pelham (public gaoler of Williamsburg and organist at Bruton Parish Church) thanks L.C. for sending Major John Griffin's pis-

tol for his Commission. Conveys
the governor's expression of appreciation for L.C.'s excellent service as commander of the county
militia.   [128]

1769 Dec. 25. CHARLES CARTER,
"Corotoman," to L.C. ALS. 1 p.
End.
    L.C.'s nephew gives his uncle
an account of business before the
Assembly. In the letter he expresses doubt that anything immediate would be done regarding the
bill regulating the practice of
innoculation.   [129]

[177—]. REV. ISAAC W. GIBERNE
to L.C. ALS. 2 pp. End.
    The rector expresses a differ-
ence of opinion with L.C. on some
current political issue.   [130]

[177—]. L.C. to [   ]. ALS. 2 pp.
    In this draft of a letter to a fel-
low American, L.C. discusses the
effects of "popularity" as a means
of influencing the will of the people. (L.C. was greatly opposed to
the new methods of soliciting
votes.)   [131]

[177—]. [L.C.] to JOHN BOUGH-
TON. ALS. 6 pp. End.
    This is a letter from L.C. to his
overseer at "Rings Neck" directing
him to provide the negroes with
one shirt or shift and one pair of
shoes. He writes at length about
the best method of cultivation of
tobacco, of applying manure, the
control of worms, and other planting problems. He also gives detailed instructions for building a
water mill. ("Rings Neck" was
L.C.'s York County plantation.)
                            [132]

[177—]. L.C. to WILLIAM RIND,
Williamsburg. AD. 4 pp.
    In this incomplete draft of a
letter for publication, L.C. de-
fends the efforts of colonists to
protect their traditional rights as
Englishmen.   [133]

[177—]. L.C. to "ROBERT WORME-
LEY CARTER and FRANCIS
LIGHTFOOT LEE, REPRESEN-
TATIVES IN ASSEMBLY OF
THE COUNTY OF RICH-
MOND." AL. 2 pp.
    L.C. admonishes the newly
elected representatives to be alert
to the problems involved in the
colonies' dispute with England.
He repeats his attack on the high-
handed action of the Parliament
in which the colonies had no rep-
resentation. (Robert Wormeley
Carter and his friend Francis
Lightfoot Lee were elected to the
House of Burgesses in 1769.) [134]

[177—]. L.C. to ROBERT WORME-
LEY CARTER and FRANCIS
LIGHTFOOT LEE. AL. 6 pp.
    In this draft of a letter from
"The Several Freeholders of the
County of Richmond to Their
Representatives in Assembly," L.C.
points with alarm to the program
of carrying colonists to England
for trial.   [135]

ca. 1770. "ADDRESS TO THE
COURT, BY ONE OF THE
JUDGES." AD. 4 pp.
    L.C. is critical of the lawyers
and officers of the County Court
for delaying the business of the
court. He expresses his concern
about the responsibility of local
officers and their administration
of public affairs.   [136]

1770. CHARLES CARTER, "Coroto-man," to L.C. ALS. 1 p. End.

L.C.'s nephew declines his un-cle's invitation to keep or care for Charles's son, Hill. He states that improvement in the health of the boy precludes the necessity. In the letter Charles Carter complains of the plague of runaways. He re-quests L.C. to have outlawed sev-eral slaves owned by Charles, but who had run away while working at "Sabine Hall." [137]

[1770 Apr. 9?] L.C. to "TWO IN THE CORNER." AD. 3 pp.

In this letter written for publi-cation, L.C. refers to himself as "C-R." The letter deals with astro-nomical observations and makes special reference to the "current discussions of the Transit of Ve-nus [1769]." (See April 13, 1770.) [138]

1770 Apr. 13. WILLIAM RIND, Wil-liamsburg, to L.C. ALS. 1 p.

The editor of the *Virginia Ga-zette* acknowledges L.C.'s letter of April 9 signed "C-R." He regrets the impossibility of immediate publication of the letter owing to the shortage of paper and the great number of such letters being written. (See item 138.) [139]

1770 May 14. GEORGE MASON, "Gunston Hall," to "MESSRS. LANDON CARTER and CHARLES CARTER, EXECU-TOR OF COL. CHARLES CAR-TER, DEC'D." ALS. 3 pp. End. by L.C.: "Left me with the answer."

George Mason requests reply to an earlier letter offering to buy the "Broad Run" tract of the Charles Carter estate at a rate of

£28 sterling per 400 acres. He en-closes a copy of the letter of March 15 to Charles Carter, Jr. [140]

1770 June 8. R[OBERT] WORME-LEY CARTER, Williamsburg, to L.C. ALS. 1 p. End.

The son of L.C. discusses effects of the dry weather on the crops at "Rings Neck." He states that he was returning L.C.'s wig, which had been sent to the shop for re-pair. (Young Carter was in Wil-liamsburg to attend his first ses-sion of the Assembly.) [141]

1770 June 17. ROBERT [WORME-LEY] CARTER, Williamsburg, to L.C. ALS. 1 p. End.

Robert Wormeley Carter re-ports that he had placed an order for shoes in the hands of "Mr. Gil-bert's shop." He sent by bearer of the letter an old chocolate pot, "apprehending that a new one might embarrass you." [142]

1770 June 22. R[OBERT] WORME-LEY CARTER, Williamsburg, to L.C. ALS. 1 p. End.

This letter was written from the House of Burgesses. Young Carter reports a legislative struggle over the Tobacco Bill, which included a provision to reduce salaries of the Inspectors on the Rappahan-nock Creek. He also reports that the merchants of the Colony had come into the Association for Free-dom, and thus were cooperating in the efforts to administer the Non-Importation agreement. [143]

1770 July 25. GRIFFIN GARLAND, Surveyor, to L.C. ADS. 1 p. End.

A plat and description of the

tract known as "Juggs," part of the "Sabine Hall" estate. [144]

1770 Aug. 3. JOHN TAYLOE to L.C. ALS. 1 p. End.

This letter reports the fatal wounding of several horses and requests that L.C. determine if any of his servants had been involved. [145]

[1771?] [L.C.] to *VIRGINIA GA-ZETTE.* ALS. 6 pp.

A draft of a letter prepared for publication. In the letter L.C. argues against the proposal to include plantation overseers in the militia draft. He insists that, without overseers, the slaves would in their idleness plot their own freedom or the destruction of their masters. He points out the folly of drafting overseers to fight one enemy and in so doing remove the protection from an enemy even more bloody. In closing he refers to himself as "a steady friend of society in every instance of justice, good order, and humanity." [146]

1771. REV. ISAAC W. GIBERNE, "Belle-Ville," to L.C. ALS. 1 p. End.

He requests that L.C. send some cauliflower and radish seed and some raspberry slips. In exchange the rector sent L.C. some lettuce seed. [147]

1771 Feb. 13. FRANCIS LIGHT-FOOT LEE to L.C. ALS. 1 p. End.

He regrets that an invitation to Col. William Fauntleroy's would prevent his coming to "Sabine Hall" for a social affair to which he had been invited. [148]

1771 Mar. 4. MASTER LANDON CARTER, "Corotoman," to L.C. ALS. 1 p. End.

While attending school at "Corotoman" young Landon Carter requests that his grandfather send a copy of *Robinson Crusoe.* He expresses hope that his father, Robert Wormeley Carter, would get him a British grammar. [149]

1771 Mar. 6. RALPH WORMELEY, JR., "Rosegill," to L.C. ALS. 1 p. End.

The letter accompanied a book which was being returned. In closing, the writer passes on the rumor that Lord Dunmore was to become governor. [150]

1771 Mar. 31. JOHN TAYLOE to L.C. ALS. 1 p. End.

L.C.'s neighbor comments on the building of a fence on the line between the two estates "as shall even defy a deer to get over." He complains that L.C.'s patrolmen were not doing their duty, permitting Tayloe's slaves to ramble about during the night. [151]

1771 [Sept.] REV. ISAAC W. GIBERNE, "Belle-Ville," to L.C. ALS. 4 pp. End.: "Not in defense of a sassy fool, but seemingly to indulge him."

The rector attempts to have L.C. and Dr. William Mortimer cease their persistent bickering. The inference of the letter was that Dr. Mortimer had refused to answer a call to "Sabine Hall." This quarrel between L.C. and the doctor grew out of L.C.'s insistence that he be informed in detail about the medicine prescribed by the physician. [152]

1771 Sept. 23. JOHN TAYLOE, Norfolk, to L.C. ALS. 1 p.

This is a statement which reports an amount (£80.1.1) L.C. owed Col. Robert Tucker's estate. [153]

1771 Oct. ROBERT WORMELEY CARTER to L.C. ALS. 1 p. End.

L.C.'s son reports sending the physic L.C. had requested for the negro quarters and the medicines ordered for his own use. These included ". . . Elizar, Signorice, Ginange, Camphorated spirits, Balsam Peru, Eye water Brandy, Pepermint, etc. . . ." [154]

1771 Oct. 15. ROBERT CARTER NICHOLAS, Williamsburg, to L.C. ALS. 1 p. End.

Fragmentary. [155]

1771 Nov. 10. MASTER LANDON CARTER, at "Corotoman," to L.C. ALS. 2 pp. End.

Young Landon Carter thanks his grandfather for the clothing which had been sent. He reports that the writs had been published in church the previous Sunday and that the election was to be held on November 25. In closing he comments on his suffering with the ague. [156]

1771 Dec. ROBERT WORMELEY CARTER, "Corotoman," to L.C. ALS. 2 pp. End.

The father of Landon Carter II reports on the rapid recovery of the young man, who had had a prolonged attack of the ague and fever. Robert Wormeley Carter gives a detailed account of the treatment of the patient and medicine used. (See November 10, 1771.) [157]

1771 Dec. 20. WILLIAM FITZHUGH, "Chatham," to L.C. ALS. 2 pp. End.

L.C.'s nephew thanks him for the favor and reports on general health of the family. [158]

1771 Dec. 21. OWEN GRIFFITH to L.C. ALS. End.: "Written purely to show how much a villain he could be."

In a letter addressed to "Boisterous Tyrant," the writer acknowledges his guilt of some act for which he was forced to quit Virginia. He does not mention L.C.'s role in the affair. [159]

1771 Dec. 23. ROBERT BEVERLEY, "Blandfield," to L.C. ALS. 2 pp. End.

The husband of L.C.'s daughter, Marie, reports on the general curiosity as to the type of governor Lord Dunmore would make. He expresses his views as to the qualities needed in a man for such an office. [160]

1772 Mar. 20. R[OBERT] WORMELEY CARTER, Williamsburg, to L.C. ALS. 1 p. End.

L.C.'s son reports on the progress of business in the Assembly, noting particularly that the bill to remove the seat of government to Richmond Town, on the land of Richard Adams, had been debated and passed in the House, but was expected to be defeated in the Council. He also mentions that a bill for docking entails by fine and recovery had not been passed by the Council, as he had hoped it would not. (Such letters were the means by which L.C. kept in touch with affairs in the Assembly.) [161]

1772 Mar. 30. REV. ISAAC W. GIB-
ERNE, "Belle-Ville," to L.C. ALS.
1 p. End.

The rector reports a visit with
Dr. Walter Jones at Cherry Point
and of the latter's intention to set
up practice in Richmond (County).
He referred to his having sent a
"discourse" to L.C. the day before
and expresses his appreciation
for L.C.'s judgment. (Dr. Walter
Jones became an important social
and political figure in Richmond
County.)   [162]

1772 Mar. 31. REV. ISAAC W. GIB-
ERNE to L.C. ALS. 1 p. End.

The rector thanks L.C. for an
invitation to visit "Sabine Hall,"
but declines because he was in the
process of working his vineyard
and could not trust anyone else
to do the work.   [163]

1772 Apr. 2. DR. WALTER JONES,
"Belle-Ville," to L.C. ALS. 1 p.
End.

After acknowledging the receipt
of a message from L.C., the doctor
reports that he was in the process
of moving to his new quarters in
Richmond.   [164]

1772 June 4. REV. ISAAC W. GIB-
ERNE to L.C. ALS. 3 pp. End.

In a very involved letter, the
rector requests L.C. to write to
Edward Montague (agent for the
Assembly in England) and enlist
his favor with the Earl of Sandwich to in turn request of his good
friend, the Bishop of London, for
the appointment of the writer as
Commissary of the Colony. He
also asks L.C. to use his influence
with the important people of the
Colony and encourage them to
write to their friends in England

to speak to the Bishop about the
matter. (See June 5, 1772.)   [165]

1772 June 5. L.C. to EDWARD MON-
TAGUE, London Agent. ALS. 3
pp. End.

In compliance with the letter
from Isaac Giberne, L.C. presents
a strong plea to Edward Montague
that the latter use his influence
with the Bishop of London in behalf of the rector. (See June 4,
1772.)   [166]

1772 Aug. L.C. to WILLIAM RIND
[*Virginia Gazette*]. ALS. 6 and 7
pp.

These are two signed drafts of
letters on the subject, "Whether
a Member of His Majesty's Council Should be Served with a Sum-
mons to Answer before any Court
in the Colony but that of the
County in Which He Lives or the
General Court." In his argument
L.C. holds that members of the
Council had no such immunity,
basing his position first on mere
justice to commoners, and second
on a detailed interpretation of
the law of the Colony.   [167]

1772 Sept. 24. RALPH WORMELEY,
JR. to L.C. ALS. 2 pp. End.

Thanks L.C. for inquiring into
the health of a young lady in
whom the writer was deeply interested. He reports his inability
to obtain certain books for L.C.
                                  [168]

1772 Oct. RALPH WORMELEY, JR.,
"Rosegill," to L.C. ALS. 4 pp.
End.

The writer acknowledges receipt
of a letter in which L.C. had reported his investigation of a
Greek word. (L.C. maintained
an interest in the classics from

the period of his schooling in England.) [169]

1772 Nov. 13. L.C. to WILLIAM FAIRFAX, "Greenway Court," ALS. 5 pp. End.

In a detailed letter L.C. disputes the accounting of his quit rents bill. He argues that his manner and means of paying such bills had been misrepresented and necessitated his writing directly to the proprietor. (See April 10, 1760; August 20, 1766; and July 12, 1768.) [170]

1772 Dec. 4. DR. WALTER B. JONES to L.C. ALS. 1 p. End.

The doctor thanks L.C. for his offer of beef and promises to attend the annual Christmas entertainment at "Sabine Hall." [171]

1772 Dec. 20. CHARLES CARTER, "Corotoman," to L.C. ALS. 1 p. End.

Reports attendance at an auction sale at Rocky Ridge, "where slaves, stocks, ferry, warehouses, fishery, etc. was sold to advantage, but as ten thousand pounds was the highest offer for the land, they are not yet disposed of." Informs L.C. of his willingness to sell his land on the "Fork" for £40 sterling on 12 months credit. [172]

1773 Jan. 9. CHARLES CARTER, "Corotoman," to L.C. ALS. 2 pp. End.

The son of Charles Carter writes to his uncle and reports his inability to find among the land papers of his grandfather (Robert "King" Carter) the deed of conveyance from Robert Carter, Jr. to Robert Carter, Sr. for a certain tract of land. (The ownership of this tract was the basis of a dispute between Col. Charles Carter and Robert Carter of "Nomini Hall.") In his letter Charles Carter mentions finding among the land papers of Robert Carter, the Elder, a deed of conveyance from his son for 11,375 acres of land constituting another tract. [173]

1773 Feb. 22. JOHN TAYLOE, "Mount Airy," to L.C. ALS. 1 p. End.

The writer comments on a visit of John Page of "Rosewell." [174]

1773 Feb. 22. JOHN TAYLOE to L.C. 1 p. End.

In this letter Col. Tayloe refers to some land scheme of L.C.'s as being of doubtful wisdom, even though "no man is obliged to part with his property even to please a governor." He felt that the plan would only irritate the governor and thus cause trouble later. (The details of the plan were not discussed.) [175]

1773 June 10. "TITHABLES BELONGING TO LANDON CARTER IN LUNENBERG PARISH IN RICHMOND COUNTY, June 10, 1773." ADS. 1 p. End.

The list included L.C., George Mengrica, William Beale, Jr., John Selfe, James Pursell, Walter Harris, and 68 slaves. (The tax was paid on all adult males and all slaves more than sixteen years of age.) [176]

1773 Aug. [ ]. REV. ISAAC W. GIBERNE to L.C. ALS. 2 pp. End.

The rector attempts to quiet L.C.'s wrath at some comment made by a neighbor. In closing he refers to L.C.'s birthday (August 18) as "being last week." [177]

1773 Aug. 23. JOHN WORMELEY, Lancaster, to L.C. ALS. 1 p. End.

The writer recommends to L.C. the bearer of the letter as an overseer.   [178]

1773 Aug. 25. DR. WALTER B. JONES to L.C. ALS. 2 pp. End.

The doctor apologizes for not attending L.C.'s birthday feast. He refers to some "disturbance" occuring at the party, where someone had spoken falsely of Dr. Jones' regard for L.C. (L.C.'s birthday feast and the Christmas celebration were the main social events at "Sabine Hall.")   [179]

1773 Sept. 18. RALPH WORMELEY, "Rosegill," to L.C. ALS. 1 p. End.

L.C.'s friend regrets the inability to send L.C. any tobacco. (During this period a reduction in tobacco production caused the planters financial difficulties.) [180]

1773 Oct. L.C. to WILLIAM RIND. ALS. 4 pp. End.

This is a signed copy of an article prepared for publication. In the article, L.C. attacks the proposed levy of 3 shillings per hogshead of tobacco. He asks nine specific questions involving such a levy and requests that the members of the Assembly answer them. He fears the effects such a levy would have on the specie situation in the Colony.   [181]

1773 Nov. 6. ROBERT WORMELEY CARTER, Williamsburg, to L.C. ALS. 1 p. End.

L.C.'s son reports progress in carrying out minor chores for the family while in town. He reports that the Secretary of the Colony

has requested payment of money which L.C. has owed for two years.   [182]

1773 Dec. 19. CHARLES CARTER, of "Corotoman," to L.C. ALS. 1 p. End.

The nephew writes that he could not assist his uncle's overseer in moving L.C.'s wheat to the landing, since his carts would be in use "making provision for the holy days, when all hands are to play for a whole week according to custom." He sends his regrets at the news of the death of his aunt, Lucy Carter Fitzhugh.   [183]

ca. 1774. [L.C.] to "MY FRIEND." AL. 5 pp.

This is a draft of a scathing letter to someone who had inferred (1) that L.C. had on several occasions caused him harm, and (2) that L.C. had accepted a bribe from the "friend's" father at some past election. In his letter L.C. gives some interesting sidelights on his early elections to the House of Burgesses.   [184]

1774 Feb. 14. [L.C.] to [ALEXANDER] PURDIE and [JOHN] DIXON, Williamsburg. AL. 7 pp. End.

This is a draft of a letter for publication in answer to a letter signed "Cosmopoli" which had appeared in the Gazette. The latter had criticized the Boston Tea Party. In his reply L.C. presents two major points: (1) that public writers should take great care in writing about "that sacred subject —Liberty," and (2) that for America to submit to a tax on tea would open the door for Parliament to raise revenues by taxing any or all imports. In closing he states that "the price of tea so imported is certainly our whole liberty." [185]

1774 Apr. 23. JOHN TAYLOE, Williamsburg, to L.C. ALS. 1 p. End.
This is a letter thanking L.C. for ordering the correction of one of Tayloe's slaves. Included also in the letter is the report that Governor Dunmore had hoped to see L.C. [186]

1774 May 3. ROBERT WORMELEY CARTER, from Hobbs Hole, to L.C. ALS. 1 p. End.
The writer reports settling a disputed bill and sending the receipt to his father. (The name of the town of Hobbs Hole was later changed to Tappahannock.) [187]

1774 May 7. RALPH WORMELEY CARTER, Williamsburg, to L.C. ALS. 1 p. End.
This is an account of the events of the first few days of the 1774 session of the Assembly. [188]

1774 May 8. RALPH WORMELEY CARTER, Williamsburg, to L.C. ALS. 1 p. End.
L.C.'s son reports having the overseer at "Rippon" send him a horse since his had been badly kicked by that of Nat, L.C.'s servant. He reports also that in his shopping he has been unable to find a suitable toothpick box for L.C. [189]

1774 May 10. RALPH WORMELEY CARTER to L.C. ALS. 1 p. End.
This is a further comment on the dullness of the Assembly session. He also reports that William Jackson, overseer at "Rippon,"

had come to town in pursuit of a wench who had failed to carry out some instructions, "upon which he turned up her clothes and whipped her breach; I checked him for his mode of correction and made the matter up between them." [190]

1774 May 13. REV. ISAAC W. GIBERNE, "Belle-Ville," to L.C. ALS.
In this letter the rector attempts to have L.C. repent his sworn enmity for the young man (Reuben Beale) who had eloped with L.C.'s daughter, Judith. On the outside of the letter Giberne has written, "don't fling this in the fire as there is gold in it." In the endorsement L.C. comments, "I would have thrown this in the fire but for this false representation [   ] by the writer." (The marriage referred to was a very happy one, but L.C. never completely forgave the young man for his actions.) [191]

1774 May 19. DR. WALTER B. JONES to L.C. ALS. 1 p. End.
This is a humorous note which includes a comment by Dr. Jones on L.C.'s stroke and includes some philosophical comments about the health problems of the declining years. [192]

1774 June 17. DR. WALTER B. JONES to L.C. ALS. 3 pp. End.
The doctor, who had become interested in politics, reports the activity at a public meeting held at Farnham. According to the report, the common people felt that since they did not drink tea they were not involved in the colonial dispute. In the letter the writer asks if L.C. could not be persuaded to call such a public meeting. [193]

1774 July 10. MOORE FAUNTLE-
ROY, "Crandall," to L.C. ALS.
1 p. End.

L.C.'s neighbor reports that his
house had been broken into and
that some rum had been stolen.
He asks if L.C. would make inquiry among his negroes regarding
the theft.   [194]

1774 July 18. L.C. to *VIRGINIA GA-
ZETTE.* AL. 4 pp. End.: "Foul
or rough of copy sent [Alexander]
Purdie July 18. If he will print it."

In this article L.C. presents a
defense of the Boston Tea Party.
After commenting on the seriousness of the situation he observes,
"I certainly feel that if I am not
to be free life must be a burden
to me, and that he who takes my
liberty from me must be an equal
enemy to my life." (See August 3,
1774.)   [195]

1774 Aug. 3. ALEXANDER PURDIE,
Williamsburg, to L.C. ALS. 1 p.
End.

The editor of the *Gazette* reports that he had printed 40 copies of L.C.'s article signed, "Expe-
rienced," (July 18). These had
been printed at cost and thirty
copies had been sent to various
gentlemen and ten copies to L.C.
                              [196]

1774 Sept. 11. ARCHIBALD RITCH-
IE, Leeds, to L.C. ALS. 1 p. End.

The writer, a storekeeper, reports sending some letters to L.C.
by the pilot boat from Leeds. [197]

1774 Oct. 27. MINUTES OF A MEET-
ING OF THE COUNTY [OF
RICHMOND] COMMITTEE
RESPECTING THE ASSOCIA-
TION FOR AMERICAN FREE-

DOM. DS. 2 pp. End. Copy by
Leroy Peachey, Clerk.

The report lists those present
as being L.C., William Fauntleroy,
John Smith, William Brockenbrough, Robert W. Carter, Francis
Lightfoot Lee, John Belfield, Daniel Muse, Jonathan Beckwith,
Leroy Griffin, William Miskell,
Charles McCarty, William Colston, Hudson Muse, John Sydnor,
Samuel Hipkins, John Fauntleroy,
William Smith, and Leroy Peachey,
"Gentlemen." L.C. was unanimously elected chairman of the
committee and Leroy Peachey,
clerk. As one of its first items of
business the committee appointed
a group of the members to call
upon those in the County who had
not signed the Association papers
and to report to the committee the
names of any who refused. (See
December 5, 1774.)   [198]

1774 Dec. 1. "HIS MAJESTY'S MOST
GRACIOUS SPEECH FROM
THE THRONE." D. 2 pp. End.

This copy of the speech had
been sent by W[   ] Dennes of
London to the Rev. Mr. Giberne,
who gave it to L.C. In his comment on the back, L.C. refers to
the speech as "Father George play-
ing the American dead march."
                              [199]

1774 Dec. 5. "ANNOUNCEMENT OF
SELECTION OF DELEGATES
TO THE CONTINENTAL
CONGRESS BY THE FREE-
HOLDERS OF RICHMOND
COUNTY." AD. 1 p. Written by
L.C. as Chairman of the Associa-
tion and sent to Alexander Pur-
die, Printer, Williamsburg.

The December 5 meeting selected 28 men, "convenient in

their situation" to represent the Association in the County. (A meeting held January 2 elected Robert Wormeley Carter and Francis Lightfoot Lee as delegates to the Philadelphia Convention.) [200]

1775. "A LIST OF SOULS ALIVE IN THE FORKS OF TOTUSKY 1775." Prepared by John Sydnor, addressed to the "Chairman or Clerk of the Committee of Richmond County." AD. 2 pp. End.

The census lists 69 families and indicates for each the number of persons in each of the following categories: white males upwards of 16 years (88), white males under 16 (84), black males upwards of 16 (56), black males under 16 (86), white females (173), black females (154). (An interesting statistical picture of the area.) [201]

[1775] DR. W[ALTER] B. JONES to ROBERT WORMELEY CARTER. ALS. 2 pp. End. by L.C.

The doctor reports that a Capt. [   ] Layton had arrived to collect contributions from the people of the Northern Neck to aid the people of New England. [202]

1775 Feb. 21. A[LEXANDER] PURDIE, Williamsburg, to L.C. ALS. 1 p. End.: "A pretty compliment. . . ."

The editor acknowledges receipt of the resolutions of the Richmond County Committee, and L.C.'s article on making molasses. In closing he promises to print any article which L.C. might choose to submit. [203]

1775 Feb. 25. L.C. to RICHARD HENRY LEE. ALS. 1 p. End. by L.C.

This is a draft of L.C.'s comment on a pamphlet loaned him by Richard Henry Lee. L.C. criticizes particularly the author's suggestion that there was a difference between taxation without representation and legislation without representation. In his view, "to separate or distinguish taxation from legislation without representation is only to palm an argument for the sake of that supremacy claimed by Parliament." [204]

1775 Apr. 28. L.C. to "THE INDEPENDENT COMPANY OR COMPANY OF VOLUNTEERS OF RICHMOND COUNTY." AL. 2 pp.

In this draft of a letter L.C. expresses his encouragement to those who had helped in the recovery of the munitions which had been removed from the local magazine by the governor. L.C. feels that they had been justified in recovering what was rightfully theirs, but admonishes them to be content with the measure. [205]

1775 Apr. and May. L.C. to "[   ]." AL. 3 and 4 pp. End.

These two drafts of a letter were evidently written to a Britisher, to whom L.C. refers as "my dear Parent." This is a detailed discussion of the colonial position in the colonial conflict. L.C. lays the total blame to the unwise administration by the Ministry. He refers to the long standing affronts to the colonists, to the efforts by the British to raise an army in the Middle Colonies against New England, to the battle of Lexington, and to the removal of the Virginia munitions from the magazine at Williamsburg. He concludes with the statement: "If you don't like this truth burn it and be warmed by it if you can. If you do like it do what you will with it."   [206]

[1775 May 12]. [L.C.] to [ALEXANDER] PURDIE. AD. 4 pp.

This is a draft of the Richmond Committee's reaction to Governor Dunmore's address to the Council, May 1, and to the Council's reply of May 3. (Printed in *Virginia Gazette* May 19, 1775.)   [207]

1775 July 29. ROBERT WORMELEY CARTER, Richmond Town, to L.C. ALS. 1 p. End.

L.C.'s son relates, "partly from conjecture," the activities of the Committee of Ordnance of the Convention meeting in Richmond. He comments on plans for an election to an annual convention and the election of a general for Virginia. He discusses plans for gathering troops and assigning them to duty or to encampment in their local districts and the proposal to "send a few young gentlemen to learn the art of war."   [208]

1775 Aug. [   ] GRIFFITH to L.C. AL. 1 p. End.: "_____ between G of the East, D of the West and their agents N_____ and F_____."

This is intended to be a whimsical lampooning of King George and Lord Dunmore.   [209]

1775 Aug. 5. ROBERT WORMELEY CARTER, Richmond City, to L.C. ALS. 2 pp. End.

Writing from the gallery of the Convention, Robert Carter expresses his disgust at the proceedings by stating, "We are of as many different opinions as we are men. . . . We are undoing one day what we did the day before." He reports that Patrick Henry had been elected Commander in Chief and Col. Nelson to command a second regiment, and William Woodford a third. He also reports plans to call up 3,000 regulars and to organize companies of "minute men" in each of 12 districts. In his comments on the political scene, Carter reports the decision to deny places in the Convention to officers of the Regular Army, Continental Congress, or Committee of Safety, or to those holding positions of profit under the Crown.   [210]

1775 Aug. 10. ROBERT WORMELEY CARTER to L.C. ALS. 1 p. End.

This is a further report of activity in the Convention. He gives special attention to the attitude which the members had toward Patrick Henry and his principles and reflects the fears of the more conservative members.   [211]

1775 Aug. 17. REV. ISAAC W. GIBERNE, from "The Cage," to L.C. ALS. 2 pp. End.

The rector excuses himself from attendance at L.C.'s birthday feast.   [212]

1775 Aug. 17. L.C.'s POEM, "Addressed to Sleep." AD. 1 p. End.

This poem is written in Latin with the prose translation in "American." L.C. notes that the poem has appeared publicly but does not indicate the publication.   [213]

1775 Oct. 13. ALEXANDER PURDIE to L.C. ALS. 4 pp. End.

The editor of the *Virginia Gazette* regrets that a shortage of paper has made it impossible to print L.C.'s address to the freeholders of Richmond County. [214]

1775 Oct. 14. DR. WALTER B. JONES to L.C. ALS. 2 pp. End.

Dr. Jones regrets that the pressure of work prevented his visit to "Sabine Hall." He expresses his disturbance at the news that L.C. had been affronted by the new leaders of the County and had decided to retire to private life. [215]

1775 Oct. 16. DR. WALTER B. JONES to L.C. 1 p. End.

This is a friendly note in which the doctor passes on information of a colonial victory over regular troops in an engagement in New England. [216]

1775 Nov. 1. ALEXANDER PURDIE to L.C. ALS. 4 pp. End.

The editor explains to L.C. the method of sending the paper from Williamsburg to "Sabine Hall" by way of Urbanna. [217]

1775 Nov. 4. JOHN PAGE, Vice-President of the Committee of Public Safety, to THE CHAIRMAN OF THE LANCASTER DISTRICT COMMITTEE. ALS. 1 p. End.

Reports opinion of the Committee relative to the replacement of an officer who has died. [218]

1775 Dec. 5. L.C. to A COMMITTEE OF THE HOUSE OF BURGESSES. AD. 2 pp. End.

This proposed resolution was sent to the committee appointed by the Burgesses to reply to Lord Dunmore's Proclamation issued from on board the "William." The resolution sharply attacks Lord Dunmore for the hypocrisy of his Proclamation in that the Governor had charged the colonists with forming an army and sending it against him without mentioning the self-preservation motive involved in the action. The resolution further scoffs at the plea that the colonists return to a state of law and order under martial law. [219]

1776 Jan. 16. DR. WALTER B. JONES to L.C. ALS. 2 pp. End.: "Carried by Col. Washington."

The doctor sends his regrets that something in a former letter has upset L.C. [220]

1776 Apr. 14. [MAJOR] JOSIAH PARKER, Williamsburg, to L.C. ALS. 1 p. End.

This letter, from a friend of L.C., comments on activities in Williamsburg and comments on politics within the Virginia Convention. He observes that "we all know the determination of the Richmond freeholders—strange times indeed." [221]

1776 Apr. 22. RALEIGH COLSTON to L.C. ALS. 1 p. End.

Writing at 10 o'clock at night, the young neighbor reports that a colonial ship captured earlier by a British tender had run aground in the Rappahannock River opposite the Colston plantation as it was being convoyed away. He proposes that a few armed men get together to capture the prize and draw it into the Colston wharf; there they could be reinforced by 14 or 15 negro hands who would help repel raiders until the militia arrived. (In the endorsement L.C. made no comment on his reactions to the letter.)   [222]

1776 Apr. 27. JOHN UPSHAW, Chairman of the Committee for Sussex, to L.C., Chairman of the Committee for Richmond. ALS. 1 p. End.

The writer acknowledges receipt of the request and resolves from the Richmond County Committee and promises to forward the resolves of Sussex Committee relative to the New England schooner, "Two Sisters."   [223]

1776 June 11. REV. ISAAC W. GIBERNE to L.C. 2 pp. End.

The rector reports the activities of a day spent at an auction. [224]

1776 July 19. LANDON CARTER, JR. to L.C. ALS. 1 p. End.

L.C.'s grandson regrets his inability to procure molasses for L.C. at Colchester, all of it having been bought to make rum. (This was a common plight among the people of Virginia at this time.) He reports that the wheat crop was light, but that the flax was good and expresses his intention to learn that business as "I see too many naked people around me."   [225]

1776 July 19. REV. ISAAC W. GIBERNE to L.C. ALS. 1 p. End.

This is an attempt to cheer up L.C. Reports that the wife of Moore Fauntleroy had said "she would rather spend a day with Colonel Carter than with any of ye young fellows." (The neighbors were concerned that L.C. was alone so much during this period.)   [226]

1776 Sept. L.C. to [ALEXANDER] PURDIE. ALS. 4 pp.

In this letter L.C. attempts to caution the public, and particularly the leaders, about the serious consequences of the crucial scarcity of money, even paper money, and the disappearance of trade. He further questions the wisdom of Congress in promising to pay off part of the loans in June 1777.   [227]

1776 Sept. 16. BETTY RANDOLPH, Williamsburg, to L.C. [her uncle]. ALS. 1 p. End.

L.C. is informed by his niece that she has sent her people to boil salt at "Rippon Hall," and asks L.C. if her doing so met with his approval.   [228]

1776. PLAT OF GUINN ISLAND [Gloucester County]. D. 1 p. End.

L.C. notes on the margin: "Guinn Island taken from a map brought here by Mr. [   ] Neale which Mr. [   ] Reynolds sent him." The notations indicate the location of friendly and enemy troops deployed for action. [229]

[1777]. L.C.'s OBSERVATIONS ON THE SURRENDER OF BURGOYNE TO GATES [Oct. 17, 1777]. AD. 2 pp.

Carter questions whether the general should have been allowed to surrender on the terms reported.   [230]

1777 Apr. 20. PHILIP KEY, Captain of St. Marys County, to RICHARD LEE, Lee Hall, readdressed to L.C. ALS. 1 p. (Seal in perfect condition.)

Captain Key reports that General William Howe's army was on

the move and that the conjecture was that he aimed for the Eastern Shore of Virginia. He reports further that a ship loaded with 500 pounds of tobacco was ready to sail for France "if the enemy will wait and give us a chance." In commenting on affairs in Virginia, he states that enlistments had improved, and that a law had been passed providing for the purchase of the time of all male servants at a price not to exceed £16. Richard Lee in a note added to the letter reports that 9,800 stands of arms had arrived at Portsmouth, New England and that a French 50-gun ship had accompanied the shipment as a convoy. [231]

1777 June. "A LIST OF ACTS PASSED IN ASSEMBLY MAY AND JUNE 1777." AD. 1 p. End. L.C. lists 17 of the acts. [232]

1777 Oct. 22. L.C. to "THE WORSHIPFUL THE COURT MARTIAL OF RICHMOND COUNTY." ALS. 4 pp. End.

This is a remonstrance to the courtmartial prompted by the efforts of the recruiting captain to draft William Beale, L.C.'s miller, even though the law exempted millers. It had been rumored that if L.C. could get Beale exempted he would make all of his overseers millers. L.C. fears that the court would act on the rumor and violate the law in his case. [233]

1778 May 4. "EXTRACT OF A LETTER FROM SAMUEL CHASE, ESQ., MEMBER OF CONGRESS, TO GOVERNOR JOHNSTON [Thomas Johnson] OF MARYLAND." Addressed to "Mr. Carrie" [?] D. 2 pp.

Here are outlined the contents of two treaties between France and the United States. The writer also comments on the expected reaction to the treaties by the people of the other countries of Europe. (There was no comment to indicate how L.C. obtained the letter.) [234]

1779 Feb. "AN INVENTORY OF THE ESTATE OF LANDON CARTER, ESQ. DEC'D. TAKEN FEB. 1779." D. 6 pp.

This inventory includes the following: slaves in Richmond County (181), delivered to Reuben Beale prior to inventory (6), in King and Queen County (12), in Westmoreland County (1), in York County (34), in Northumberland County (74), in Fauquier County (7), in Stafford County (33), in Loudon and Prince William counties (56). Total 401 negroes. It listed also stocks, tools, etc. in York County, King and Queen County, and Richmond County and a room by room inventory of the contents of "Sabine Hall." [235]

[ante 1779]. [L.C.] AD. 1 p. End.

This is a draft of a petition to the "several inhabitants of the County of Richmond," urging them to join in a protest against a proposal to divide "from river to river" the counties of Richmond, Westmoreland, King George, and Stafford. [236]

[ante 1779]. [L.C.'s] "PROPOSAL TO ESTABLISH A SCHOOL IN LUNENBERG PARISH IN THE COUNTY OF RICHMOND. . . ." AD. 4 pp.

L.C. proposes the establishment

of a school to serve 40 boys who were to study English, writing, arithmetic, Latin, Greek, etc.

[237]

[ante 1779]. [L.C.'s] MEDICAL OB-SERVATIONS. AD. 1 p.

In this essay L.C. presents his views of the effects of fluids in the body.   [238]

[ante 1779]. [L.C.'s] ESSAY ON THE CULTIVATION OF HOPS. AD. 16 pp.

In this paper L.C. discusses the choice of land, preparation of the soil, seasons for planting, harvesting, etc.   [239]

[ante 1779]. LANDON CARTER'S METHOD OF MAKING HAR-NESS FOR OXEN AND HORSES. AD. 2 pp. End. by L.C.

These directions were written by L.C. and present a step-by-step method of making harness from bull hide. The memoranda include also a sketch of a two wheeled cart.   [240]

[ante 1779]. MISCELLANEOUS EIGHTEENTH-CENTURY PA-PERS, UNIDENTIFIED AND UNDATED.   [241]

PART TWO

BIOGRAPHICAL SKETCH OF
COLONEL LANDON CARTER

I

COLONEL LANDON CARTER OF "SABINE HALL"

TO THOSE INTERESTED in the history of America in the colonial period, Landon Carter (1710-1778) is important both as a personality and as a typical representative of the ruling class of eighteenth-century Virginia. In this brief study an effort is made to assess the nature of the position which Colonel Carter occupied in his society and the manner in which he carried out his role.

The pattern of life in colonial Virginia differed, in some cases radically, from that in the other colonies. In New England and the Middle Colonies life tended to revolve about the urban centers and the family farms. In Virginia, with its terrain dissected by rivers and streams, the people had been encouraged from the early days of settlement to acquire and develop self-sufficient estates. In order to operate profitably such an establishment, it was necessary for the owner to have access to extensive tracts of land and an adequate supply of cheap labor. During the seventeenth century these requirements were met by the exploitation of the unsettled areas, the expansion of the slave labor force, and the development of tobacco as a profitable cash crop.

By 1700 this economic system had come to dominate every aspect of the life of the people in the area. Under such a system the mark of success rested on those who demonstrated the greatest ability in acquiring and administering large estates. Success meant not only the accumulation of wealth in the form of land and slaves, but also the assumption of the responsibilities which accompanied that wealth. Thus, in a manner reminiscent of the feudal period in England, there developed in Virginia a class of landed gentry conscious of the peculiarities of their system and dedicated to its preservation.

One characteristic of such a social system was the effort to maintain the unity of the large estates by keeping the ownership of the land within the family. Customs implementing such an effort became established very early in Virginia, so that by 1700 in the eyes of society and before the law of the colony a man's station and responsibilities were indicated by the family to which he belonged.

In attempting to understand the position Landon Carter held in the society of his day, therefore, it is necessary to know something of his family background. In a study of the great families of Virginia, Jackson T. Main made the following statement:

The wealthiest family estate (in Virginia) was that of the Carters, of whom seven were among the forty richest men. The Carters had together over 170,000 acres, 2340 slaves, 450 horses, 2300 cattle, in addition to thirty carriage wheels, and various town houses and lots, their total worth being almost £500,000.[1]

These are statistics. The real story lies in the manner in which this material wealth was amassed, the personalities whose efforts made it possible, and the way in which it was employed. It is against this background that the real stature of Colonel Landon Carter should be measured.

The founder of the family to which Landon Carter belonged was known in the area as John Carter of "Corotoman." He came to Virginia in 1649 as an immigrant, but obviously not a penniless one.[2] After a brief stay in Upper Norfolk, he moved to Lancaster County in the Northern Neck and quickly achieved a place for himself. Elected to the House of Burgesses in 1654, he in time earned the title of "Colonel John Carter of Lancaster County."[3]

Of the many children born to him by his five wives, his two sons

---

[1] Jackson T. Main, "The One Hundred," *William and Mary College Quarterly*, Ser. 3, XXI (1954), 364.

[2] Louis Morton, *Robert Carter of Nomini Hall* (Princeton, 1941), p. 23.

[3] Virginia (Colony), General Assembly, House of Burgesses, *Journals, 1619-1658-59*, ed. H. R. McIlwaine, 94.

are the best known. John Carter, Jr., prominent in county and colony affairs, should have been heir to his father's estate, but died without male issue, thus paving the way for his younger brother, Robert.

This young man, who came to be referred to as Robert "King" Carter, was born in 1665 at "Corotoman," heir by his father's will of 1,000 acres of land and one-third of an estate valued at 1,000 pounds sterling.[4] When he died in 1732, he left to his heirs "300,000 acres of land, 1,000 negroes, and 10,000 pounds sterling."[5] According to his epitath he was

Speaker of the House of Burgesses under four monarchs, Treasurer of the Colony, Speaker of the Assembly for 6 years, Governor for one year, liberal supporter of the College of William and Mary, husband of two wives and the father of many children.[6]

To his first wife, Judith Armistead, the following children were born: John, Elizabeth, Judith, and Anne. His second wife, Elizabeth Landon Willis, bore him eight more children, Robert, Sarah, Ludlow, Charles, Landon, Mary, Lucy, and George.[7] Of these children, the sons carried on in the father's tradition while the daughters increased the renown of the family by marrying well.

The marriage of Elizabeth, the oldest daughter, to Nathaniel Burwell produced four children: Lewis, Carter, Robert, and Elizabeth. The daughter married William Nelson, president of the Council; their son, Thomas, was a signer of the Declaration of Independence. Elizabeth Carter Burwell married a second time, to George Nicholas, to whom she bore a son, Robert Carter Nicholas, treasurer of the colony of Virginia, and Elizabeth Nicholas, who married Edmund Randolph, later attorney general of the United States.[8]

Robert "King" Carter's daughter Anne married Benjamin Harrison and had three children; of these, Anne married William Randolph, and Benjamin became a signer of the Declaration

---

[4] P. A. Bruce, ed., "Will of John Carter," *Virginia Magazine of History and Biography*, II (1894), 236.

[5] Louis Morton, *Robert Carter of Nomini Hall*, p. 23.

[6] *Ibid.*

[7] Edmund J. Lee, *Lee of Virginia, 1642-1892* (Philadelphia, 1895), p. 358.

[8] Morton, *Robert Carter of Nomini Hall*, p. 21.

of Independence and the father of William Henry Harrison, ninth President of the United States.[9] The other three daughters of Robert Carter also married well; Judith married Mann Page of "Rosewell," and Mary became the wife of George Braxton of "Newington." Lucy, by her marriage to Henry Fitzhugh, became the mistress of "Eagle Nest" in Hanover County.[10]

There is a saying in the Carter family that the genius of the clan is transmitted by the girls rather than by the boys, and this third generation suggests ample basis for such an observation. In keeping with the fashion of the time, however, it was to his sons that Robert Carter looked to carry on the estate. In a 40-page will he provided well for all of his male heirs, but in such a manner that he could be certain that the estate would be maintained.[11] According to the original bequest, the bulk of the estate was left to his eldest son, John, and to the second son, Robert. Because Robert died one month before his father, an act of Assembly set aside that portion of the will. Robert's share was passed on to his son, Robert III, then an infant, and was held in trust for him by his three uncles, John, Charles, and Landon Carter.[12]

John, as the eldest son, became known as "John Carter of Corotoman." Because of his marriage in 1725 to Elizabeth Hill, he was also known as "John Carter of Shirley." He was a worthy son of his father, serving on the Council of the Colony from 1724 to 1742[13] and as Secretary of State for the Colony from 1722 to 1743.[14]

Robert Carter, Jr., through the influence of his father, was appointed in 1727 "Naval Officer of the Rappahannock River and Receiver of Virginia Duties."[15] This post he passed on to his

---

[9] Morton, *Robert Carter of Nomini Hall*, p. 22.

[10] *Ibid.*, pp. 21-22.

[11] William G. Stanard, ed., "Carter Papers," *Virginia Magazine*, V (1898), 408-428; VI (1899), 17-21; VII (1900), 455.

[12] Virginia (Colony), Laws, Statutes, *The Statutes at Large . . .* , ed. William Waller Hening (Richmond, 1820), IV, 454.

[13] Great Britain, Public Record Office, *Journal of the Commissioners for Trade and Plantations, 1742-1749* (London, 1931), 38.

[14] William Glover and Mary Newton Stanard, comp., *The Colonial Virginia Register* (New York, 1902), p. 21.

[15] Virginia, *Calendar of Virginia State Papers*, ed. W. P. Palmer (Richmond, 1875), I, 212.

younger brother, Charles, two years later. As has been noted, Robert, Jr. died in 1732, and his portion of the estate was developed by his son, who came to be referred to as "Robert Carter of Nomini Hall." He, like the other Carter men, had been well trained for his role in the colony, and in 1758 was appointed to the Council by the Lords of Trade and Plantations.[16]

Charles, as the third son of Robert "King" Carter, inherited the plantation called "Cleve" on the upper Rappahannock River and tracts in Northampton and Lancaster Counties. Following in the footsteps of his father, he speculated heavily in land and at one time had control of vast areas in the Northern Neck.[17] Also like his father, he assumed his responsibilities to the community, serving for over thirty years as a member of the House of Burgesses.[18]

By the will of Colonel Robert Carter the two younger sons were to be educated by their three older brothers out of the revenues from the estate. Both sons were left estates in fee simple, and in addition inherited vast tracts entailed in such a way that, should one die, the other would receive both shares of the inheritance.[19] Thus the death of the youngest son, George, in 1741 materially affected the position of Landon Carter as a man of property.

Like other men of his time and station, Colonel Landon Carter measured his material wealth in terms of land and slaves. Like his kinsmen and neighbors in Virginia, he appeared to have an insatiable thirst for greater and greater holdings. This in part was due to the exploitative method of farming, which compelled the planter to acquire land for future as well as for current use.[20] The anticipated need for new land was particularly pronounced in eighteenth-century Virginia, where tobacco, the staple crop, was notorious in its demand for fresh soil.

---

[16] Great Britain, *Journal of the Commissioners for Trade and Plantations, 1759-1763* (London, 1935), 122.

[17] Fairfax Harrison, "The Will of Charles Carter of Cleve," *Virginia Magazine*, XXXI (1923), 42.

[18] Stanard, *Colonial Virginia Register*, pp. 108-167.

[19] Stanard, "Carter Papers," *Virginia Magazine*, VI (1898), 17; Harrison, "Will of George Carter," *Virginia Magazine*, XV (1908), 426-427; *Virginia, The Statutes at Large*, V, 300-302.

[20] Oliver Perry Chitwood, *A History of Colonial America* (New York, 1931), p. 449.

In addition to what might be considered a natural desire to increase his acreage, the Virginia planter was addicted to extensive speculation in land. In this field the Carters were no more acquisitive than their neighbors and contemporaries, but partly through their own efforts were more successful than most. From the time of King Charles II to 1776 the Northern Neck of Virginia had been developed under a proprietorship, and during the greater part of the first quarter of the eighteenth century Landon Carter's father had been the resident agent of that vast domain.[21] As such, he was able to grant extensive tracts to his sons and his friends, in addition to those he acquired for himself.

This practice of acquiring grants of land in the name of minor, and sometimes infant, sons created an amazingly complex land tenure system, and provided the basis for numerous suits in court, but in the case of the Carters it was the means by which the bulk of the family estate was amassed. The provisions of the settlement of the estate of George Carter give some clue to the scope of this operation, and also to the nature and size of Landon Carter's inheritance. A study of this settlement showed that in 1731 George Carter had been granted 3,310 acres in Prince William and Fairfax Counties; 2,941 acres in Prince William County, and 6,943 acres in Prince William County, as his share of a tract of 41,660 acres granted to Landon Carter, George Carter, Lewis Burwell, Carter Burwell, Robert Burwell, Mann Page and Carter Page. In addition, George Carter had been granted another tract of 3,865 acres in Frederick County. This was his share of a tract of 50,202 acres granted to Landon Carter, George Carter, Carter Burwell, Robert Burwell, Carter Page, Robin Page, Benjamin Harrison, Robert Carter Nicholas, and Robert Carter, Jr.[22] These recipients, it will be noted, were the younger sons and grandsons of the proprietor's agent, Robert "King" Carter.

It would be difficult to more than estimate the actual extent of Landon Carter's holdings during his lifetime. As has been noted, great tracts of land had been granted in his name while he was yet

---

[21] Fairfax Harrison, *Virginia Land Grants* (Richmond, 1925), pp. 93-104.
[22] Virginia, *Statutes at Large*, V, 300-302.

a schoolboy, and the records show that from the time of his majority he continued to acquire by inheritance, purchase, grant, and lease. At the same time he was selling tracts and providing estates for his sons and grandsons.

Through the gifts and bequest of his father he acquired the initial part of the "Sabine Hall" estate and two tracts known as "Mangorick" and "The Forks" in Richmond County, the "Rippon Hall" and "Rings Neck" plantations in York County, a plantation in Northampton County, and tracts in Prince William County.[23] In addition to these holdings, the records show that in 1731 Landon Carter owned a tract of 895 acres on the Shenandoah River,[24] and in 1733 had bought 624 acres in Westmoreland County.[25] In 1743 he acquired 44,294 acres from Lord Fairfax, probably for speculative purposes.[26] Whether or not this venture was profitable to Carter is not known, but the proprietor gained little by it. By 1772 the unpaid quit rent bill amounted to £678.17.3 and, so far as the records indicate, this account was never settled.[27]

Not all of this acreage was kept under cultivation. Throughout his adult life, Landon Carter considered the "Sabine Hall" estate his "home place" and centered his main planting activities there. The plantations in York County were equipped and operated as working units under the direction of overseers and were profitable sources of revenue. With the exception of scattered tracts that were worked sporadically, probably the vast majority of the property was maintained either for future use or for speculation.

Along with land, the number of slaves owned served to indicate the relative economic status of the eighteenth-century Virginia planter. In this category, Landon Carter maintained a respectable position in the Carter family and a place of prominence in the colony. A study of the records and of the advertisements in the *Virginia Gazette* reveals that Landon had no compunctions regarding the in-

---

23 Lee, *Lee of Virginia*, p. 360.

24 Surveyor John Warner prepared map and description of this tract. Map in Sabine Hall Collection, Univ. of Va., dated May 8, 1731. (Hereafter referred to as SHColl.)

25 Indenture of release, May 29, 1733. SHColl.

26 George W. Fairfax to Landon Carter, April 10, 1760. SHColl.

27 Thomas Bryan Martin to Landon Carter, July 12, 1768. SHColl.; Willard F. Bliss, "The Rise of Tenancy in Virginia," *Virginia Magazine*, LVIII (1950), 428.

stitution of slavery and bought and sold negroes freely. This fact also makes difficult any accurate estimate of the size of his holdings.

In 1773 Landon Carter reported having 68 slaves over 16 years of age in Richmond County.[28] An inventory of the estate made after his death shows best the extent of his slave holdings and, by indicating their deployment, gives a clue to the relative intensity with which the various tracts of land were utilized. This list shows 181 slaves held in Richmond County, 6 delivered to Reuben Beale prior to the inventory, 12 in King and Queen County, 1 in Westmoreland, 34 in York, 74 in Northumberland, 7 in Fauquier, 33 in Stafford, 56 in Loudoun and Prince William, a total of 401.[29]

This figure is significant when it is checked against the findings of the United States Census Bureau in 1790. This study reported that only 15 persons in Virginia owned more than 100 slaves, three times that many had from 55 to 99, and at least 40 times that number had from 5 to 9.[30]

According to the traditions of eighteenth-century Virginia it was not enough that Carter amass such a fortune for its own sake. As a member of the landed gentry he assumed three major obligations. The first of these was to produce and provide for a family to carry on his estate and traditions; the second was to develop as much of the virgin land of the colony as could be done with profit to himself and his community; and the third was to serve as a leader in his community, which to him meant parish, county, colony, and nation. The intensity of his feelings toward the responsibilities of his position goes a long way in explaining, if not justifying, his manner of operation and his attitude toward the people and events of his day.

In viewing the family of Landon Carter in terms of this scheme of things, it certainly must be assumed that he fulfilled his first obligation. He did produce a family that was a credit to his name, and he more than adequately provided for its members.

In 1730, shortly after returning from years of schooling in England, he built "Sabine Hall" in Richmond County and began to

---

28 Tithes list, June 10, 1773. SHColl.
29 Inventory of the estate of Landon Carter, February 1799. SHColl.
30 Morton, *Robert Carter of Nomini Hall*, 101.

assume the responsibilities of a local squire. In 1732 he married Elizabeth, the daughter of John and Elizabeth Wormeley of "Rosegill."[31] Within the next few years four children were born to the young couple.

The first son and principal heir to his father's estate was Robert Wormeley Carter (1734-1798). His descendants have maintained "Sabine Hall" down to the present time.[32] In spite of considerable friction between the two, young Robert seems to have followed rather closely in his father's footsteps. At the age of 21 he married Winifred Travers Beale of Richmond County, settled down at "Sabine Hall," and began to assume a position of responsibility in the community.[33] Along with Francis Lightfoot Lee, he served in the House of Burgesses as representative from Richmond County from 1769 to 1775,[34] and was a member of the Richmond Convention in 1775[35] and a member of the House of Delegates from 1775 to 1787.[36]

Elizabeth Wormeley Carter bore three other children, Elizabeth Wormeley, who became the wife of Nelson Berkeley of "Airwell," Landon, Jr., who married Judith Fauntleroy, and John, who married Janet Hamilton.[37] These two younger sons, as befitting their station, were provided with tracts of land in the back country of Prince William County by their father, and in addition fared handsomely in his will.[38]

In 1740 Landon Carter's first wife died, leaving him with four small children, so two years later he married again. His second wife, Marie, daughter of William Byrd II of "Westover," lived only three years after her marriage but gave Carter another daughter.[39]

---

[31] Lyon G. Tyler, "Extracts from Diary of Col. Landon Carter," *William and Mary Quarterly*, Ser. 1, XIII (1904), 45.

[32] Randolph Carter and Olive Marion, *The Carter Family Tree* (Richmond, 1897). [Lithographed chart.]

[33] Louis Morton, "Robert Wormeley Carter of Sabine Hall," *Journal of Southern History*, XII (1946), 346.

[34] Stanard, *Colonial Virginia Register*, pp. 184, 186, 189, 192, 194, 197, 200.

[35] Virginia (Colony), Convention, December 1, 1775, *The Proceedings of the . . .* (Williamsburg, 1776), p. 3.

[36] Morton, "Robert Wormeley Carter," *Southern History*, XII (1946), 347.

[37] Carter, *The Carter Family Tree*.

[38] *Richmond County Will Book*, No. 7, pp. 337-343.

[39] *The Virginia Gazette* (Williamsburg), December 12, 1745.

Marie Carter married Robert Beverley, of "Blandfield," a marriage quite in keeping with her illustrious parentage.[40]

Less than a year after the death of Marie Byrd Carter, Colonel Carter married a third time, this time to Elizabeth Beale, daughter of Thomas and Elizabeth Beale of Richmond County.[41] To this marriage, four more children were born. The first of these was Judith who, when she grew up, enraged her father by eloping with her cousin, Reuben Beale.[42] The second was Lucy, also a spirited young girl, who married William Colston. The other two children born to the marriage of Landon Carter and Elizabeth Beale apparently died while quite young.[43]

This record makes it abundantly clear that Colonel Carter fulfilled his first obligation, that of producing a family. The tragically early deaths of his first two wives, however, appear to have left a mark on him. Up to the time of his second wife's death, he seemed to have been engrossed in his activities as a planter, developing and adding to the "Sabine Hall" estate and expanding his holdings generally. From that time forward he became increasingly involved in political affairs, seeking a seat in the House of Burgesses and writing innumerable articles and letters. His marital misfortunes also may help to explain the irascibility that so characterized his later years and made such a poor accompaniment to his generosity and concern for his fellow man.

---

[40] Tyler, "Extracts from Diary of Col. Landon Carter," *William and Mary Quarterly*, Ser. 1, XIII (1904), 45.

[41] Tyler, "Extracts from Diary of Col. Landon Carter," *William and Mary Quarterly*, Ser. 1, XIII (1904), 45.

[42] Rev. Isaac W. Giberne to Landon Carter, May 13, 1774. SHColl.

[43] Carter, *The Carter Family Tree*.

II

AN EIGHTEENTH-CENTURY
VIRGINIA GENTLEMAN

B Y VIRTUE of his wealth and family position, Colonel Landon
Carter was recognized as an influential member of the landed
gentry of eighteenth-century Virginia. Like many men of his class
he was conscious of the nature of his position, jealous of its pre-
rogatives, and sensitive to its demands. True to his traditions, he
gave of himself generously to all the people around him but de-
manded in exchange their loyalty and respect. He was, in fact, an
interesting combination of great humanitarian and snob, probably
best described in his own words, "I am, sir, to my country and to
the whole of mankind, according to their respective subordinations
a most devoted servant."[1]

In his relations with people he demonstrated an imperiousness
coupled with an extremely sensitive pride. As a young man he was
referred to as "an impatient fellow" but a good man when he was
"in a cool temper."[2] His desire to serve and his insistence upon being respected applied to all those around him, to his family, servants, neighbors, and members of the government.

There is ample evidence that he had a real love and affection
for his children, but it is also quite clear that they were not spared
the effects of his dominance and his sensitivity. Relations between
Robert Wormeley Carter and his father seemed to have been par-

---

[1] Landon Carter to William Rind, *Virginia Gazette,* November 19, 1772.

[2] John Randolph to Landon Carter, March 3, 1735. Lee Papers, Virginia Historical
Society, Richmond, Virginia.

ticularly strained. According to his diary for 1766, the heir to "Sabine Hall" threatened to leave home to avoid "being compelled to live with him who told me I was his daily curse."[3] At the same time his father was complaining in his diary about the lack of filial respect on the part of his oldest son.

His daughter, Elizabeth, and her husband, Nelson Berkeley of "Airwell," had constant difficulty in keeping the Colonel convinced that they maintained the proper attitude. On March 17, 1765, Nelson Berkeley wrote a brief but pointed note to his father-in-law, urging him "not to do the Berkeleys the injustice of questioning their respect and gratitude."[4]

The younger daughters, Lucy and Judith, certainly received their share of parental attention. In his diary for September 18, 1770, Colonel Carter, then 60 years old, wrote the following observation on Lucy:

Miss Lucy went to John Beale's child's christening, and kept my chariot all night, went then to Cap't. Beale's. And yet the girl pretends she never goes abroad. I almost think she is seldom at home.[5]

Daughter Judith really tempted fate when in the spring of 1774 she eloped with her cousin, Reuben Beale. Her father promptly announced his sworn enmity for the fellow. When the rector of the parish wrote to Carter and attempted to have him repent, the Colonel sat down and penned a two-page commentary on the rightness of his position.[6] On May 2 Captain William Beale, the young man's father, sent Carter two dozen trout. The diary records the Colonel's reaction to the peace offering. He indicated that he was not in the mood to be mollified, and wrote:

Yet as he has shewed a kindness to the family, indeed his blood relations by the marriage of his daughter [Elizabeth] to my son [Robert Wormeley], I thanked him in their behalf, and ordered a bushel of Bernard Creek oysters to be returned. I shall not eat of these fish, and

---

[3] Morton, "Robert Wormeley Carter," *Southern History*, XIII (1946), 347.

[4] Nelson Berkeley to Landon Carter, March 17, 1765. SHColl.

[5] Landon Carter Diary, September 18, 1770. SHColl. (Hereafter referred to as LC Diary.)

[6] Rev. Isaac W. Giberne to Landon Carter, May 13, 1774. SHColl.

have only behaved consistent with my determined reflections to have no intimacy or connection [with them].[7]

Even the men of God were not immune from his wrath when they failed to pay the proper respect.[8] In 1762 a local minister threatened to sue the Colonel for defamation as a result of a comment which Carter had made in one of his writings.[9] This should have caused Landon Carter to pause, for some years earlier he had lost a battle with the clergy. The Reverend William Key, pastor of the Lunenburg Parish from 1745 to 1752, did not conceal his concern for the Colonel's haughty attitude. When he dared to preach a sermon on "Pride," Carter swore vengeance and vowed that he would "clip the wings of the whole clergy in the colony." Backed by a majority of the vestry, he nailed up the pulpit and the windows and doors of the church, and forbade the people to enter. The congregation rallied behind the pastor, broke open the church and took the pastor in. At that point Carter and his friends seized the parish glebe and leased it out to three men, who drove off the parson's cattle. Reverend William Key sued the Colonel and obtained from the jury a settlement of £30 sterling. When the case was appealed to the Privy Council in England, the decision went in favor of the parson, and Carter had to pay both the damages and the cost of the suit.[10]

This incident did not affect Landon Carter's active role in the church nor his concern for spiritual affairs. In an entry in his diary, he recounted an episode that reflected not only something of his own attitude but was also an interesting glimpse of the Reverend Isaac Giberne.

This day being a Sacrament day appointed by our minister, as a Church Warden I had all the elements and plate ready. We had notice to begin at 11. The Parson came there about 10, read prayers, and was gone before anybody but a few was there, and said it was 11 minutes after

---

[7] LC Diary, May 2, 1774. SHColl.

[8] Giberne seemed to have been the only man from whom Carter would accept criticism.

[9] John Tayloe to Landon Carter, October 16, 1762. SHColl.

[10] Lyon G. Tyler, "Library of Rev. William Key," *William and Mary Quarterly*, IX (1901), 165.

11 o'clock by his time. I got there 25 minutes after 10 with my family and got back before 11. Col. Lee came to church after me, and was at my house before 11. I am content; the Gent. entertains me when he pleases to go into the Pulpit, and I said nothing. God knows I went to commemorate the love and passion of my divine redeemer, and if his servant was otherwise disposed, I hope it is to be imputed to some other cause than my neglect.[11]

To those living in that sparsely settled area of the Northern Neck, neighborliness was a matter of serious concern, and the record showed that Colonel Carter lived up to the accepted standards. There were, however, occasions on which he acted in a way that must have been a real trial to even his closest friends. In 1763, for example, William Brockenbrough wrote to Carter, regretting that the Colonel had killed his neighbor's hogs before they could be fenced, and asking that hereafter they should be sent home if they happened to trespass.[12] There appears to have been constant bickering between Carter and the John Tayloes of "Mount Airy." In his diary for November 3, 1770, the Colonel commented that "Col. Tayloe's overseer, a vile fellow, always abroad, lets the hogs wander." And on November 5, 1768, he received a letter from Rebecca Tayloe thanking him for the fine breast of venison, but accusing him of shooting the deer in the Tayloes' deer park.[13]

One of the constant problems facing the eighteenth-century Virginia country squire was that of obtaining the services of men capable of supervising the work on the plantation. Landon Carter seemed to have had considerable worry in this regard, although he did not have any great turnover among his overseers. He was accustomed to giving them explicit instruction and then keeping a critical eye on their activities. In 1757, when he employed an overseer for one of his plantations, he stipulated that

he is to follow all my directions in everything, he is to have 500 wt. fresh pork, milk of two cows, what corn his family can reasonably eat and £25 current money the year, he is not to go abroad without my leave and to use every kind of diligence.[14]

[11] LC Diary, October 25, 1772. SHColl.

[12] William Brockenbrough to Landon Carter, September 8, 1763. SHColl.

[13] Rebecca Tayloe to Landon Carter, November 5, 1768. SHColl.

[14] LC Diary, September 13, 1757. SHColl.

In April 1771 he commented that his overseer, John Beale, appeared diligent, "but must be something harebrained."[15] And in February 1774 he wrote, "Billy Beale off this day to 'Lovershall,' my Northumberland plantation. I do suppose that his brother, the overlooker there, may be miffed at it, but I cannot bear to make nothing there with such fine lands and such good hands."[16] At another time he wrote:

William Lawson went up to take possession of my Park Quarters Thursday, the 15th of the month. He is to get things in order, and to bring all my hogs to fatten here, for that rascal, Brown, not only sold all my last crop of corn, but even did not intend to make any this year; for he never wed the little he tended; neither did he ever work my tobacco.[17]

As a slave owner Landon does not appear to have been any better nor any worse than his contemporaries. He looked upon his negroes as valuable pieces of property, to be provided for and kept in good repair, and to be adequately punished when they failed to serve or disrupted the work of the plantation. He wrote to his overseer at "Rings Neck" and instructed him to provide his slaves with one shirt or shift and one pair of shoes, and not to pamper them "as does my son."[18] He was mindful of their illnesses and disabilities, but was furious when they took advantage of any special treatment. At one time he ordered that his "wenches with child" should not be required to carry heavy burdens on their head or shoulders; sometime later he wrote concerning this arrangement, "now they will scarcely work at all and then only close by their homes."[19] He seemed to have given a number of privileges to his personal servant, Nassau, who on one occasion took advantage of his position by getting drunk and staying hidden for an entire day. As a consequence, the Colonel put handcuffs on him and locked him up until he could "find time to correct him."[20]

This objective approach seemed to Carter to be the correct one

---

[15] *Ibid.,* April 17, 1771.
[16] *Ibid.,* February 19, 1774.
[17] LC Diary, October 19, 1774. SHColl.
[18] Landon Carter to John Boughton, 177[ ]. SHColl.
[19] LC Diary, March 28, 1771. SHColl.
[20] LC Diary, September 17, 1770. SHColl.

to take in dealing with slaves. On the night of June 25, 1776, twelve of the "Sabine Hall" negroes ran away to join Lord Dunmore. Prior to their leaving the estate they ransacked the house, taking guns and ammunition, Landon, Jr.'s silver buckles, George's shirt, and Tom Parker's new waistcoat, but did not touch a single item belonging to the Colonel. This fact he attributed to having always kept the slaves in their places.[21]

Accompanying this sternness and implacability, Landon Carter possessed a spirit of generosity and obligation that has been noted earlier. Throughout his adult life he found himself responsible for the welfare of a great many people. Probably the first of these burdens was his share in the trusteeship of the estate of young "Robert Carter of Nomini Hall." From 1734 to 1749 Landon Carter and his two brothers were responsible by law for the management of this vast estate, as well as for the education and training of the young master.[22] This stewardship appeared to have been faithfully carried out, for the estate prospered and a lifelong friendship was maintained among the four men. Even after young Robert had become a figure of prominence in the colony and a member of His Majesty's Council, he exhibited a great respect and affection for his uncle, Landon Carter.[23]

When Charles Carter of "Cleve" died in 1764, he left a vast number of acres, children, and debts. In Charles Carter's will, his brother, Landon Carter, was appointed one of the executors of the estate and the guardian of the testator's children.[24] Judith Banks, sister of Charles Carter's first wife, made her home at "Cleve" and seemed to have taken charge of the domestic scene, but was dependent on Landon Carter for guidance and resources. In June 1765 she wrote to Colonel Carter and urgently requested money with which to buy shoes for the children and the negroes. Indicating that this was more than an ordinary call on an executor, she commented on all the trouble which Charles Carter's affairs had

---

[21] *Ibid.,* June 26, 1776.

[22] Morton, *Robert Carter of Nomini Hall,* pp. 30-34.

[23] Robert Carter to Landon Carter, January 21, 1764. SHColl.

[24] Harrison, "The Will of Charles Carter of Cleve," *Virginia Magazine,* XXXI (1923), 69.

caused.[25] In another letter she expressed her gratitude for all that Landon Carter had done for the orphaned children of his brother and at the same time solicited his patience with "the tempers of the children."[26]

There were times when "Sabine Hall" must have had the appearance of a combination hospital and boarding school. The Colonel maintained a tutor most of the time for the education of his own children, his grandchildren, and his nieces and nephews. In 1772 he advertised in the *Virginia Gazette* for a tutor for his six grandsons, whom he wanted "grounded in Grammar, Writing, and Arithmetic."[27] In addition, he maintained a charity school on the estate for the education of the less fortunate children in the area.[28]

Partly because of his keen interest in the science of medicine and partly because there was no one else to do it, Colonel Carter assumed full responsibility for the care of the sick at "Sabine Hall." Taking into account the 150 to 200 negroes, the adult whites, and the swarm of children who lived there, this task was expensive and time-consuming. It must be remembered also that both the black and the white populations of eighteenth-century tidewater Virginia suffered chronically from dysentery, malaria, and "agues and fevers," as well as from the ordinary childhood diseases. At one time the Colonel wrote:

I have now my daughter Lucy, grandchildren Fanny, Betty, and Lucy, and Wormeley Carter and his sister Molly ill. Little Lucy's measles very full out. Her Aunt Lucy, my son Landon's daughter, and Mary Carter, Lucy's sister, and their maid, Grace, all broke out.[29]

In the field of medicine Colonel Carter had both a practical and a theoretical interest. His diary and correspondence contain what were almost clinical notes on the symptoms of his patients, the treatments he used, and the rate of recovery. The extent of his interest in the diagnosis and treatment of the diseases of the area led him into chronic conflict with the local doctors. After appar-

25 Judith Banks to Landon Carter, June 23, 1765. SHColl.
26 Judith Banks to Landon Carter, March 22, 1766. SHColl.
27 *Virginia Gazette,* March 12, 1772.
28 LC Diary, August 4, 1770. SHColl.
29 *Ibid.,* February 1, 1774.

ently forcing one physician to leave the community, he proceeded to make life difficult for the successor, Dr. John Mortimer. In 1771, when this physician refused to give the Colonel a detailed account of the contents of his prescriptions, Carter forbade him to come to "Sabine Hall."[30]

His interest in medicine went beyond that of the ordinary planter concerned with keeping his slaves in working condition. His writings contain numerous items dealing with the subject of theoretical medicine. For example, in his papers there is a little essay of a highly technical nature concerned with the "Effects of Fluids in the Body,"[31] and in the *Virginia Gazette* of December 3, 1772, there appeared a long article of his, advocating measures to control the plague imported on convict and slave ships.

Colonel Carter felt that the demands put upon him by his family and community constituted the normal lot of the landed gentleman. He liked to refer to himself as "a steady hand to society in every instance of justice, good order, and humanity."[32]

By training and tradition he was prepared to lend such a hand to society. As a typical member of the landed gentry of his day, he demonstrated that he had the knowledge and skill required of the farmer, surveyor, engineer, doctor, and judge. His understanding of law and government and his ability in political exposition can best be appreciated by a study of his work as a legislator and writer during the period of the Revolution.

However, a search of his papers and correspondence reveals a practical and serious concern in many other fields. On the margins of the March 1776 issue of the agricultural journal, *Museum Rusticum,* Colonel Carter wrote numerous notes concerning the proposed innovations in farming methods; some of these notes were caustic criticisms of new-fangled ideas, more of them were memoranda noting his intention to experiment with the new techniques.[33]

During his lifetime tobacco remained the chief cash crop of Tidewater Virginia. Migration to the interior and the necessity for finding a new marketable crop had not yet been fully realized.

---

[30] LC Diary, September 24, 1771. SHColl.
[31] Essay in SHColl.
[32] *Virginia Gazette*, March 28, 1777.
[33] Landon Carter's annotated copy in SHColl.

In his own domain, however, he carried on very serious experiments and programs in both plant and animal husbandry. Throughout his papers and correspondence are references to the raising of sheep and hogs, and he is listed as one of the Virginia gentlemen who helped develop blooded horses in America.[34] Always in search of new uses for his lands and equipment, he developed an interest in the growing of hops, bees, and grapes.[35]

By the time he had gained a seat in the House of Burgesses, he exhibited an interest not only in the development of his own land but in the advancement of the whole colony as well. In 1759 he was appointed one of the trustees of a program to pay bounties to "anyone bringing to perfection any art or manufacture of service to the public."[36] And a year later he was listed as one of the public-spirited gentlemen who annually pledged sums ranging from one to ten pounds for ten years to establish a fund from which an annual premium of £500 would be paid to the maker of the best wine in the colony.[37]

Probably Colonel Carter's most scholarly, as well as practical, contribution to the field of scientific farming was the study he made of the nature and control of the "weevil moth," a scourge to the growing of wheat in Virginia. The report of this study was printed in the *Transactions* of the American Philosophical Society in 1769, and was also published in the *Virginia Gazette* on March 19, 1775.[38]

Along with his enlightenment, however, he seems to have been somewhat apologetic for any departure from the ways of his father. In his diary for May 12, 1776, he wrote an interesting tribute to the industry of Robert "King" Carter and a criticism of "plows and carts."

I hear abundance abt plows and carts; my father never used a plow in the five years from 1727 to 1732, in which he died, except one he indulged me with at home to make a little farm of turnips, cabbages, and

---

[34] William G. Stanard, "Racing in Colonial Virginia," *Virginia Magazine*, II (1894), 301.

[35] Thomas Nelson to Landon Carter, May 26, 1763. SHColl.

[36] Virginia, *Statutes at Large*, VII, 288-289.

[37] *Ibid.*, VII, 568.

[38] Landon Carter, "Observations Concerning the Fly-Weevil . . . ," American Philosophical Society *Transactions*, I (1769), 274-287.

tares. And I believe tho his family was large and of course his expense of food great, no man ever sold more wheat or corn. I have known him year after year to load a large Bermudian, and many vessels from Norfolk came for his wheat, and as to carts, he never had but old Nassau with twelve oxen for all his plantations . . ., and he never carted from one of the sd. plantations one hhd. either light or heavey and never one apple or Peach. . . . As to wheat, each plantation aimed at 150 bushels, and this with hoes only. . . . I never used cart or plow in Northumberland till growing delicate in taste, I would have oysters brot up from thence, and then I had only one cart and each plantation kept 2 oxen. . . .[39]

Sometime prior to 1755 Landon Carter began to operate a grist mill at "Sabine Hall," not only processing wheat and corn for his own use but probably providing a service for his neighbors as well.[40] When the non-importation agreements of the 1770's caused Colonel Carter to have difficulty in finding enough cloth to cover the bodies of the scores of people dependent on him, he built a textile mill. In 1777 he advertised for a manager "well skilled in managing Hemp, Flax, Cotton, Wool, for the spinning wheel, from the growth; one who is also capable to instruct others, and conduct the Business of weaving, etc."[41]

Like many of his eighteenth-century contemporaries, he maintained an interest in activities not directly related to his work as a planter. During the later years of his life Carter devoted a considerable amount of time to the field of astronomy, not only reading books and articles on the subject but also submitting for publication his own observations. Early in 1770 he sent to the *Virginia Gazette* a long discourse on his observations dealing with the transit of Venus in 1769, a subject on which the amateur observers were in disagreement.[42]

As has been noted, Colonel Landon Carter probably made his greatest literary and intellectual contribution in the field of government and politics as he took his part in the American struggle for freedom. This contribution deserves separate and special attention.

[39] LC Diary, May 12, 1776. SHColl.
[40] William Garland to Landon Carter, October 23, 1755. SHColl.
[41] *Virginia Gazette,* June 20, 1771.
[42] Landon Carter to "Two in a Corner," [*ca.* April 9], 1770. SHColl.

III

ANOTHER RELUCTANT REBEL

A S A PROMINENT MEMBER of the landed gentry of eighteenth-century Virginia, Colonel Landon Carter was expected to assume an active part in the political life of his community. For the first twenty years after his arrival in Richmond County he confined his interests to his own parish and county. Even after he had entered the larger arena of colony affairs, his first concern was for his local area. In 1768 he wrote to the new governor, Lord Botetourt, apologizing for not waiting upon His Excellency when he arrived in the colony and expressing his best wishes for a good administration. In this letter he referred with pride to his position as Lieutenant of Richmond County, "a post held under the administrations of William Gooch, Robert Dinwiddie, and Francis Fauquier."[1]

From 1752 to 1770 he represented Richmond County in the House of Burgesses[2] and served on a number of important committees. For the first ten years of service as a Burgess he was particularly active in arousing the people to a consciousness of the dangers presented by the war with the French and the Indians. It was during this period also that he raised some of the earliest and the strongest of the protests against the treatment of the colonies by Parliament.

In order to understand the course of Colonel Carter's political

---

[1] Landon Carter to Lord Botecourt, November 1, 1768. SHColl.
[2] Virginia, House of Burgesses, *Journals, 1752-1758*, vii, viii; *1758-1761*, viii; *1762-1765*, 3, 32, 170, 202, 314; *1766-1769*, 4, 80, 136, 182.

activities, it is necessary to see clearly the philosophy of government, law, and justice by which he lived. By training and tradition he was a conservative, ever ready to challenge any attempt to usurp the political power of the traditional leaders. During the 1750's and 1760's he occupied one of the leading roles in the colony's protests against Parliamentary tyranny. From 1770, however, the record indicates that he was almost equally antagonistic to what he referred to as "republicanism." In defense of the Boston Tea Party he wrote, "I certainly feel that if I am not to be free life must be a burden to me, . . . he who takes my liberty must be an equal enemy to my life."[3] But in May 1776 he confided to his diary his fear of the mounting radicalism, "Hurray for Independency, Sedition, and Confusion."[4]

To many of his friends and to all of his enemies, his readiness to attack both loyalist and radical, and his insistence that the tyranny of Parliament was no worse than the tyranny of the Virginia Convention or the Continental Congress, appeared to be inconsistent. Whether it was or not, it cost Colonel Carter his political popularity and forced him to make his contribution to the cause of liberty through the use of his pen.

As has been noted, Colonel Carter's service to the colony in the field of politics fell roughly into two periods, the one from 1750 to 1770, the other from 1770 to the end of his life in 1778. During the first period his contribution was made as a member of the House of Burgesses, but from 1770 on his activities were those of a private citizen and as the Chairman of the Richmond Committee of the Association for Freedom.

During the period of the French and Indian War he took a strong stand on the necessity of the colony assuming its share in the conduct of the operation. In May 1757, along with John Robinson, Charles Carter, Peyton Randolph, Carter Burwell, Benjamin Waller, and James Power, he was appointed to serve as a manager and director of a lottery established to provide money for defense against the French.[5] In August of that year he was appointed one of the

---

[3] Landon Carter to the *Virginia Gazette,* July 18, 1774. SHColl.

[4] LC Diary, May 1, 1776. SHColl.

[5] Virginia, *Statutes at Large,* VI, 454.

directors of a fund of £40,000 which was to be raised for this same purpose, and in March of the next year was appointed to help direct the administration of a fund of £25,000.[6]

The leaders of the colony were far from being united in their support of the war and were not above partisanship in their striving for personal gain and advancement. On April 21, 1756, Carter wrote to George Washington, as an old friend, admonishing him not to resign his leadership of the troops because of the rumored efforts of some to replace him. At the same time he commented on the apathy of the people in their struggle against the French and Indians:

. . . Should we talk of obliging men to serve ye country ye are sure to have a fellow mumble over ye words Liberty and Property a thousand times. Sir, I think as you do, I have endeavored tho not in the field yet in the senate as much as possible to convince the country of danger and they know it. . . .[7]

Throughout the history of the colony there had been sporadic friction between the colonists and the government in England. During the period of the French and Indian War, the signs of the resentment of the colonists became more open. In 1759 the colonial leaders established a "Committee of Correspondence" and appointed Edward Montague as agent for the Assembly in its dealings with the commercial and political factions in England. William Nelson, Thomas Nelson, Philip Grymes, and Peter Randolph represented the Council on this committee, and John Robinson, Peyton Randolph, Charles Carter, Richard Bland, Landon Carter, Benjamin Waller, George Wythe, and Robert Carter Nicholas represented the House of Burgesses.[8]

Landon Carter's selection was a tribute to the position he held in the eyes of his fellow legislators. E. I. Miller, in his study of Virginia's Committee of Correspondence, made the following statement:

From the nature of the work required of the Committee, its member-

6 *Ibid.*, VI, 524; VII, 13.

7 Landon Carter to George Washington, April 21, 1756, *Letters to Washington and Accompanying Papers*, ed. Stanislaus Murray Hamilton (Boston, 1898), I, 256.

8 Virginia, *Statutes at Large*, VII, 276-277.

ship had to be selected with care. The members had to be broadminded men, men who understood the economic and political conditions in the colony, who knew the English government, who had good judgement, and who were loyal to the cause of the people.[9]

Like other men of his status, Landon Carter had for a long time resented the position of economic dependency in which the colonies were forced to exist. He was one of the first to feel that continued apathy might eventually affect their political existence as well. In 1753 he had written a caustically humorous letter, signed "Londonensis." Posing as a fictitious merchant bidding for business among Virginia planters, he attacked the questionable business tactics of the London merchants.[10]

During the latter part of the 1750's the inability of the colonists in Virginia to control their own economic affairs was made glaringly evident. For a long time tobacco had been used as a medium of exchange in that colony. In 1755 and again in 1758 unfavorable growing conditions caused a shortage in this commodity, and hence an increase in its price. If the planters were forced to pay taxes, salaries, and fees in tobacco at the established rates, they would be bearing an undue economic burden. As a consequence, the Assembly of the colony passed legislation which permitted the payment in cash of taxes, fees, and debts incurred during the lifetime of the Acts. The Acts were to be renewed annually, and the rate of exchange was fixed at two pence for every pound of tobacco that was due.[11] The clergy of the Church of England reacted violently against the legislation, reporting their grievance to the Privy Council. This body vetoed the legislation on the grounds that the Assembly had exceeded its powers, an action which launched one of the early skirmishes between colony and mother country.

Colonel Carter, as a representative from Richmond County, took an active part in the controversy. In 1759 he wrote a pamphlet in the form of a "Letter to the Right Reverend Father in God, the

[9] E. I. Miller, "The Virginia Committee of Correspondence, 1759-1770," *William and Mary Quarterly*, Ser. 1, XXII (1913), 4-5.

[10] [Landon Carter] to "The Gentlemen Planters of Virginia," October 12, 1753. SHColl.

[11] Virginia, *Statutes at Large*, VI, 568-569; VII, 240-241, 277-278.

Lord Bishop of London."[12] He conceded that the action of the Assembly in all probability had not been in keeping with the letter of the law, but claimed that "there were exceptions in all cases" and that "justice to the people and charity to the poor" made the Two Penny Act such an exception. This inflammatory outburst preceded Patrick Henry's "Liberty or Death" speech by four years and was the basis of the Colonel's later insistence that it had been he, and not Henry, who had "given the first breath for liberty in America."[13]

The end of the French and Indian War in 1763 saw the colonies and the mother country assume new attitudes toward each other. To the colonies, the successful conclusion of the war had eliminated the French menace and had reduced materially the danger of Indian attack. They felt less in need of protection by England. To England, however, the end of the war meant the achievement of a position of world power and recognition of the financial cost of that achievement, two excellent reasons for a new colonial policy.[14]

This new policy called for a new and more stringent control over imperial affairs and a search for new sources of revenue. With this in mind, Parliament in 1764 passed a Sugar Act, which was really an extension of the Molasses Act of 1733. The new law restricted the importation of rum and spirits from foreign plantations and increased the import tax on sugar. This measure raised a storm of protest in the colonies, and in Virginia the Assembly ordered a committee, of which Landon Carter was a member, to draw up an address to the King and memorials to Parliament as a means of expressing its displeasure.[15]

The ensuing months witnessed a mounting tension between the colonies and the mother country over the right of Parliament to tax those colonies. In the August 25, 1765, issue of a British paper, *The Public Ledger*, William Pym attempted to defend the action of Par-

[12] Lyon G. Tyler, "The Leadership of Virginia in the War of the Revolution," *William and Mary Quarterly*, Ser. 1, XIX (1910), 18-20.

[13] LC Diary, July 25, 1776. SHColl.

[14] Chitwood, *A History of Colonial America*, pp. 624-625.

[15] William G. Stanard, "Virginia Legislative Documents," *Virginia Magazine*, IX (1902), 367-368.

liament in this matter. On November 30 Carter, in a 24 page pamphlet, proceeded to give "a little consideration" to this article. In his detailed rebuttal the Colonel reflected not only the seriousness with which the Americans looked upon this dispute, but also indicated the manner in which the dispute had evolved from one simply dealing with an economic problem to a discussion of basic constitutional principles.[16]

By 1768 both parties to the dispute were becoming more caustic in their comments. On May 9, 1768, the House of Representatives of Massachusetts was disbanded, much to the dismay of Americans everywhere. The Virginia House of Burgesses published a circular letter in which it tried to reflect the feelings of the people of Virginia. Couched in respectful terms, the letter read, "They [the Burgesses] trust they have expressed themselves with a firmness that becomes Freemen pleading for essential rights, and with a Decency that will take off every Imputation of Faction or Disloyalty."[17] Colonel Carter was not as circumspect in a circular letter which he wrote to "The Members of the Late House of Representatives of Massachusetts Bay" in which he expressed sympathetic concern for their plight, offering encouragement to them in their struggle.[18]

Partly as a result of the increased activity on the part of the leaders of the Colony in the dispute with the mother country, there developed a change in the political atmosphere so far as the voters were concerned. Consequently, Colonel Landon Carter lost his seat in the House of Burgesses in the election of 1768, his place being taken by Thomas Glasscock.[19] His political difficulties apparently had developed even prior to that time, for in June of 1765 Richard Henry Lee wrote to him and expressed his regret at the news that the Colonel was going to retire from public life.[20] He finished out his term of office, but Judge St. George Tucker, who arrived in Williamsburg in 1772, wrote to William Wirt, "Landon Carter

---

[16] Landon Carter to "M_____," November 30, 1765. SHColl.

[17] G. Kearsley, ed., *The American Gazette* (London, 1768), No. 1, 19-22.

[18] "The Members of the Late House of Representatives of Massachusetts Bay." A circular letter dated 1768. SHColl.

[19] Stanard, *Colonial Virginia Register*, p. 179.

[20] Richard Henry Lee to Landon Carter, June 22, 1765. *The Letters of Richard Henry Lee,* ed. James Curtis Ballagh (New York, 1911), I, 7-9.

never visited Williamsburg after my arrival. His influence appears to have been considerable at some former period. . . ."[21]

From 1770 on, sometimes privately, sometimes as Chairman of the Richmond County Committee, he attacked tyranny and ineffective government, both foreign or domestic. He divided his efforts between criticizing the British ministry and exhibiting his fear that the inept strivings of the colonial leaders presented an equally grave danger to the people.

On May 29, 1770, he confided to his diary his disgust at the "dallying of the Assembly over the repeal of the Revenue Acts." He criticized the willingness of some

to meet the Parliament half . . . so whilst we were enslaved by those that were not repealed we must go our half and give up that point. Fine language this, as if there could be any half way between slavery and freedom; certainly one link of the former must be the hold to which the rest of the chain might at any time be joined, when the forging smiths thought proper to add it.[22]

He had easy access to the activities in the House of Burgesses after his son, Robert Wormeley, had regained the Carter seat in 1769.[23] Using this as a source of information, he kept a steady stream of comments flowing to his many friends and to the editors of the *Virginia Gazette.*

In October 1773, in one of his "letters to the editor," he attacked the Assembly's proposed plan to levy a tax on tobacco, holding that such a move would threaten the economy of the colony, cause the destruction of those without specie, and cause an oppressive detention of their one general staple produce.[24] After the Act had been passed he wrote to the editor of the *Gazette,* enclosing a list of nine questions on the new tax and requested that the editor publish the list and encourage the members of the Assembly to answer them.[25]

Consistent with his sense of justice, he viewed with alarm the

---

[21] Judge St. George Tucker to William Wirt, September 25, 1815, *William and Mary Quarterly,* XIII (1914), 256-257.

[22] LC Diary, May 29, 1770. SHColl.

[23] Virginia, House of Burgesses, *Journals, 1766-1769,* 222.

[24] Landon Carter to William Rind, October 2, 1773. SHColl.

[25] Landon Carter to William Rind, *Virginia Gazette,* November 13, 1773.

regulating Acts passed by Parliament in the spring of 1773. He resented particularly the import tax on tea and lauded the efforts of the citizens of Boston in their protest against the act. Colonel Carter was not the only conservative American who could be numbered with the supporters of that show of radicalism. As Edward Channing put it, "This picturesque activity of the Boston Puritans excited different emotions in their contemporaries."[26] John Adams called the "Tea Party" an "Epoch in History," and Landon Carter defended the episode against all comers.

On February 14, 1775, he penned a seven-page letter for publication in the *Gazette* in answer to one who had criticized the "Tea Party."[27] In this letter he cautioned that public writers "should take great care in the use of that sacred subject—Liberty," and attacked the writer for "unmercifully abusing those fine sons of liberty—the Bostonians." He further observed that "the price of tea so imported is certainly our whole liberty," pointing out that if America submitted to that tax it opened the door to all oppressions.

Colonel Carter felt that such oppressive Acts should be opposed by all the people and joined those who were incensed at the attitude of the common people, who, since they did not drink tea, tended to remain indifferent to the new tax.[28] This fact may well have affected the Colonel's suspicion of what he came to call "republicanism."

After 1769, when the several colonies had established associations of one kind or another to facilitate their resolutions not to import any goods on which a tax had to be paid, men like Landon Carter, working in the local communities, rendered invaluable service. The minutes of a meeting of the Richmond County Committee for October 17, 1774, reported that a group of the members had been appointed to call on those in the community who had not signed the agreements of the association and to report to the Committee the names of those who refused.[29] In September

---

[26] Edward Channing, *A History of the United States* (New York, 1912), III, 133.

[27] Landon Carter to Alexander Purdie and John Dixon, February 14, 1774. SHColl.

[28] Dr. Walter B. Jones to Landon Carter, June 17, 1774. SHColl.

[29] "Minutes of a Meeting of the [Richmond] County Committee . . .," October 27, 1774. SHColl.

1775 William Brockenbrough, William Peachey, Robert Wormeley Carter, and Francis Lightfoot Lee, under the chairmanship of Landon Carter, formulated and published in the *Gazette* a request that anyone in the community learning of any instances of violations of the Non-Importation Agreement report such information to the signers. In the same article they requested that Peyton Randolph, President of the Convention, publish the list of the Associators in the Colony.[30]

The Richmond Committee, and particularly its Chairman, did not limit its action to the carrying out of orders. According to the *Gazette* for February 17, 1775, the Committee instituted a vigorous program to suppress the smuggling of goods into the colony from ships lying off the Capes.[31] The Colonel appeared to have been particularly incensed by this type of disloyalty, referring to Hobbs Hole, the river town in his area, as "a mere nest of Tories."[32]

The months of May, June, and July in 1775 constituted a sort of turning point in the course of the dispute between the colonies and the mother country. During those months after the Battle of Lexington, the conservative program of respectful, even if obstinate, opposition to the new colonial policy broke down. During the next few months the course of events in Virginia was determined on the one hand by Patrick Henry and his rabble rousing, and on the other by the Governor, who vaccilated between timidity and unprecedented recklessness.[33]

Early in May His Majesty's Council in Virginia took it upon itself to allay the upheaval by an address "To the Good People of Virginia," calling upon them to use caution in their conduct, and forbearance with the legitimate agencies of government.[34] Colonel Carter wrote a heated reply to this address on the margins and back of his copy, and recommended to the Richmond Committee that it

---

[30] *Virginia Gazette,* September 27, 1775.

[31] *Ibid.,* February 17, 1775.

[32] Landon Carter to George Washington, May 9, 1776. *American Archives,* ed. Peter Force (Ser. 4; Washington, 1946), I, 390.

[33] Claude H. Van Tyne, *The Founding of the American Republic* (Boston, 1929), I, 199-200.

[34] Original in Carter Brown Memorial Library, Duke University; photostat in McGregor Library, University of Virginia.

express itself.[35] He evidently won his point, for on May 25, 1775, the Committee published a watered-down version of Carter's draft.[36]

On May 2, 1775, Lord Dunmore addressed the Council, setting forth for publication the royal reaction to the current disturbances, and on May 3 the Council made a limp and anti-climactic reply. To both of these addresses the Richmond Committee expressed its opposition in a statement in the *Gazette,* again a document drafted by Landon Carter and then toned down for publication.[37]

In addition to using the Richmond Committee as a vehicle for his attack on what he considered the tyranny of Crown and Parliament, Colonel Carter carried on his own war of words through private letters and articles in the *Gazette.* In a private letter evidently written to an Englishman, to whom he referred as "my dear Parent," he outlined in detail the colonial position in the struggle. He laid the total blame for the difficulties to the unwise administration by the Ministry and to its agents in America. He referred to the long standing affronts to the colonists, to the efforts by the British to raise an army in the Middle Colonies against New England, to the Battle of Lexington, and to the removal of the Virginia munitions from the magazine at Williamsburg by Governor Dunmore. In characteristic form he concluded the letter with the statement: "If you don't like this truth burn it and be warmed by it if you can. If you do like it, do what you will with it."[38]

During the first six months of 1775 affairs in Virginia gradually degenerated from a state of armed stalemate to one of open warfare. Early in June the Governor made one last address to the Assembly, made up of the Council and the members of the Virginia Convention which had been formed the previous summer. The revolutionary conventioners, acting as the House of Burgesses, firmly rejected the Governor's proposals of reconciliation[39] and expressed their disgust with the Governor himself. As the temper of

---

[35] *Ibid.*

[36] *Ibid.*

[37] *Virginia Gazette,* May 19, 1775; draft in SHColl.

[38] Landon Carter to "_____," May [ ], 1775. SHColl.

[39] Original copies of these addresses, together with annotations by Landon Carter, are in the library at Duke University. Photostatic copies are in the possession of the University of Virginia.

the people continued to mount, the Governor realized the danger of his position and fled from Williamsburg, taking refuge aboard the British gunboat, "Fowey," at Yorktown. With the departure of the royal agent, the government of the Colony fell into the hands of the Convention and its executive agency, the Committee of Safety.

The members of this Convention, all duly elected Burgesses, met in Richmond during July and August. The official records as well as the personal observations of the members reflected the struggle which went on between the radicals and the conservatives. In a letter to his father, Robert Wormeley Carter expressed his disgust at the proceedings, complaining that "we are of as many different opinions as we are men . . . undoing one day what we did the day before."[40] As the weeks wore on, the membership appeared to divide itself between the partisans of Patrick Henry and the old-line aristocrats, who were as fearful of the popular orator's ambition as they were of royal tyranny.[41]

The Governor himself helped to resolve the dilemma of the conservatives by a studied persecution of the propertied class in the Colony. Following his directions, units of British regulars and bands of runaway slaves and renegade whites pillaged the riverside plantations. On December 7, 1775, he committed a fatal blunder, so far as the hopes for reconciliation were concerned. From aboard the warship, the *William*, he published a proclamation offering freedom to all slaves and indentured servants who would turn against their masters and join the royal cause.[42] The specter of a servile insurrection threw the slaveholding population into a a panic and, whether they liked the idea or not, they saw that their only hope lay in joining forces with the radicals. All that the conservatives could do from that time on was to temporize and delay the course of events.

Colonel Carter was a typical member of that group of conservatives who only reluctantly joined the revolutionary cause and who

---

[40] Robert Wormeley Carter to Landon Carter, August 5, 1775. SHColl.

[41] R. W. Carter to L.C., August 10, 1775.

[42] Francis L. Berkeley, Jr., *Dunmore's Proclamation* (Charlottesville, Virginia, 1941), p. 3.

never became completely reconciled to the logical conclusion of such a movement.

In his particular case, Carter seemed to have singled out the little pamphlet, "Common Sense" by Thomas Paine, as either the symbol of the new order or its progenitor. For months following its appearance in January 1776, he made mention of it in almost every piece of correspondence. He wrote in his diary for February 14:

I see the Philadelphia Pamphlet "Common Sense" is much advertized in Philadelphia, and it is pretended to be written by an Englishman. If it is true, it is really much to be suspected of its secret intention to fix an ill impression that the Americans are resolved not to be reconciled, and indeed that matter is encouraged under the most absurd arguments in the world. But I do not suppose it to be the concealed topic of even some in Congress, tho they have so repeatedly contradicted and they have so severely reprehended Dr. Cooper some time ago, who actually charged them with a design of independency.[43]

In the diary for February 20, he wrote:

In a letter to Washington and Lee regarding my son Landon, I could not in both my letters help giving my sentiments on this pamphlet called "Common Sense," it is so repleat with art and contradiction, and man is represented in it as a being which ought to be not only unforgiving, but implacable to the highest degree, and he that does not so think is nothing short of a coward and sycophant, which in plain meaning, must be a damned rascal. Nay, he goes further; this implacability must be a part of that divine image which was implanted in man. . . .[44]

As Colonel Carter watched the course of events, he saw a definite connection between the chaos in the colonies, the rise of the new republican forces, and the clamor for "independency." He was particularly concerned about the changes that were taking place in his own area. It was painful indeed for the old squire to see his own kind "turned out" of their places of leadership and replaced by those who were willing to grovel before the people. On being informed that his grandson, Landon Carter, could become an aide to the commander of the Virginia forces only by paying his own

---

43 LC Diary, February 14, 1776. SHColl.
44 *Ibid.,* February 20, 1776.

expenses, he commented, "I can plainly see that the requisite cringing is so necessary that a soliciting person is now kept undetermined, that he may be tired and retire in order that a more cringing person may be engaged."[45]

Like many of his station, Colonel Carter detested the new Governor, Patrick Henry, regarding him as the very symbol of the "publican" element that had taken over in the Colony. Patrick Henry had seemed to secure for himself a place in the imaginations of the people. Not only was he credited with his own deeds of valor, but his followers attributed to him honors that rightfully belonged to others.

In one of the eulogies, he was referred to as "the one who opened the breath of liberty to America." Colonel Carter expressed his personal bitterness about this in his diary:

But it was with truth replied and Proved that that breath was breathed and supported by a person not then taken notice of. I know this merit is claimed also by another, but only say I never courted public applause; and if any endeavor assists my country, I care not who enjoys the merit of it.[46]

And later he wrote:

I asked Lee who came home with me if he had not remembered who gave the first breath of liberty to America; and he said he remembered well, and it was an absurdity to give it to P. Henry the Governor, for he was not at the Assembly, tho they gave him credit for it.[47]

During the spring of 1776 Colonel Carter became increasingly suspicious of the course of events. He agreed with the concern of Francis Lightfoot Lee over the mismanagement of public affairs in Virginia,[48] and in a letter to Washington he wrote: "I could have wished that ambition had not so visibly seized so much ignorance over the colony as it seems to have done, for this present Convention abounds with too many of the inexperienced creatures. . . ."[49]

---

[45] LC Diary, March 31, 1776. SHColl.

[46] LC Diary, July 14, 1776. SHColl.

[47] Ibid., July 25, 1776.

[48] Francis Lightfoot Lee to Landon Carter, April 9, 1776. Lee Papers, Virginia Historical Society.

[49] Landon Carter to George Washington, May 9, 1776. American Archives, ed. Force, (Ser. 4), V, 390.

He was convinced that justice, order, peace, and freedom could no longer be secured under British control, but doubted whether the program proposed in Virginia would guarantee any greater freedom.

Like many of the conservatives, Carter continued to hope that the differences between the colonies and the mother country could be reconciled. He particularly resented the headlong rush of the Virginia Convention toward independence.[50] When that convention, on May 15, 1776, unanimously instructed its delegates in Congress to strive for the establishment of an independent government, he felt that the act was as arbitrary as some perpetrated by Parliament. In his diary he wrote: .

. . . It is pretended to be a pressing occasion, which is the very first step in all despotic climax. . . . Why then is a limited monarchy objected to on account of some possible arbitrariness that may be introduced into it, and the same tendency or precedent for such a tendency, established only because it can be confidently advanced that these Republican distractions have arisen from Monarchical Principles; for my part I see no difference; an evil begot how it will and necessity is no better plea in a Republican form than it is or can be in a Monarchical form.[51]

A few weeks later he expressed his thankfulness that from the beginning of the struggle the fault had been with the Parliament and the Ministry, but repeated his fears that through the secret strivings of some of the leaders of the colonies the people might find themselves in more trouble than they had known prior to 1770. He continued to criticize those who agreed with the writer of the pamphlet, "Common Sense," for their efforts to stampede the colonies into making a complete break with the mother country. In his diary he wrote a solemn prediction:

Certainly it behooves him who admires Peace, Order, and Moderation in Government to be cautious of such people, for it is morally certain that there are such, and without the utmost timely care they will work themselves into a Hydra of Power. I don't expect to live to see it, but mark the conclusion.[52]

---

50 Landon Carter to George Washington, May 9, 1776. *American Archives,* ed. Force, (Ser. 4), V, 390.

51 LC Diary, May 23, 1776. SHColl.

52 LC Diary, May 29, 1776. SHColl.

After a state of independence had been declared on July 4, 1776, the old squire, like many others of his class, "bridled his tongue and watched his step."[53] On a few occasions after that, however, he expressed his views on public policy. In September 1776 he wrote one of his characteristic letters to the editor of the *Gazette*, in this case requesting the editor to caution the public leaders concerning the financial policies being established. He was particularly concerned about the great danger caused by the scarcity of specie and paper money. He further questioned the wisdom of the Congressional proposal to pay off part of the loans of the colonies in June of 1777, feeling that such a presumptuous act would bring certain ruin to the whole country.

By the end of the year both his health and his spirits seemed to be on the decline, and some of the changes that were being made by the new government gave him great concern. In a letter to Washington he bitterly attacked Thomas Jefferson's proposal to abolish the institution of entail. He wrote:

It is called docking all entail, but is it not entailing one they cannot dock? The curses of posterity on them who must in the very contest for liberty entail a load of debts upon those who are to come, after they have robbed them of the very estates to pay that debt from, by overturning the very principles of justice on which they built their very claim to freedom . . . this bill is as cursed in its nature as the removal of a neighbors landmark.[54]

By this and similar measures, many of the old landmarks of eighteenth-century Virginia were removed by the new order. Colonel Landon Carter was too old to anticipate a new way of life, and in all probability had been too well endowed by the system into which he had been born to have wanted a change in any event.

Throughout his life Colonel Carter lived according to the standards set by his society. As a young man he had accepted the three responsibilities of the Virginia aristocrat. The first of these was to

---

[53] Van Tyne, *The Founding of the American Republic*, I, 208.

[54] Landon Carter to George Washington, October 31, 1776. *American Archives*, ed. Force, (Ser. 5), II, 1305-1307. This bill, finally passed, was called, "An Act declaring tenants of lands and slaves in taille to hold the same in fee simple," (Virginia, *Statutes at Large*, IX, 226-227).

produce and provide for a family which would carry on his estate and traditions; the second was to develop as much of the virgin land of the Colony as would be profitable to himself and his community. The third of these obligations was to help direct the affairs of that community for the benefit of its people.

The records of the period attest to the success with which Colonel Carter had met his first two obligations. The service he rendered to the people of his parish, county, and colony constituted a fulfillment of the third. For over thirty years he worked to help maintain justice and good order in the Colony. When such conditions could no longer be secured under British rule he sincerely, though reluctantly, joined in the struggle for independence.

BIBLIOGRAPHY

BIBLIOGRAPHY

A. MANUSCRIPT MATERIAL

Landon Carter Diary, 1752-1778. University of Virginia Library.
Lee Papers. Virginia Historical Society, Richmond, Virginia.
Sabine Hall Collection, 1660-1894. University of Virginia Library.

B. OFFICIAL RECORDS AND DOCUMENTS

1. GREAT BRITAIN

Great Britain, Public Record Office, *Journal of the Commissioners for Trade and Plantations.* 14 vols. London, 1920-1938.

2. UNITED STATES GOVERNMENT

United States. *American Archives: Fourth Series. Containing a Documentary History of the English Colonies in North America, from the King's Message to Parliament of March 7, 1774, to the Declaration of Independence by the United States.* Peter Force, comp. 5 vols. Washington, 1837-1846.
United States. *American Archives: Fifth Series. Containing a Documentary History of the United States of America, from the Declaration of Independence, July 4, 1776, to the Definitive Treaty of Peace with Great Britain, September 3, 1783.* Peter Force, comp. Washington, 1848-1853.

3. VIRGINIA

Virginia. *Calendar of State of Virginia State Papers and Other Manuscripts from May 16, 1795 to December 31, 1798 Embracing the Letters and Correspondence of the Committee of Correspondence and Inquiry of Virginia and the Other Colonies from March 12, 1773 to April 7, 1775. Also the Journal of the Committee of Safety of Virginia from February 7, 1776 to July 5, 1776.* H. W. Flournoy, et al., eds. 11 vols. Richmond, 1875-1893.

Virginia (Colony) Convention. *Instructions for the Deputies Appointed to Meet in General Congress on the Part of the Colony.* Williamsburg, December 1, 1774.

Virginia (Colony) Convention. *The Proceedings of the Convention of Delegates, Held at the Town of Richmond, in the Colony of Virginia, on Friday the 1st of December, 1775, and afterwards, by Adjournment, in the City of Williamsburg.* Williamsburg, 1776.

Virginia (Colony), General Assembly, Council. *Executive Journals of the Council of Colonial Virginia.* H. R. McIlwaine, ed. 5 vols. Richmond, 1925-1930.

Virginia (Colony), General Assembly, Council. *Legislative Journals of the Council of Colonial Virginia.* H. R. McIlwaine, ed. 3 vols. Richmond, 1918-1919.

Virginia (Colony), General Assembly, House of Burgesses, *Journals of the House of Burgesses of Virginia.* H. R. McIlwaine, ed. 13 vols. Richmond, 1905-1915.

Virginia (Colony), General Assembly, Council. *Proclamation to the Good People of Virginia.* Williamsburg, May 10, 1775.

Virginia, Lancaster County. *Records.* State Library, Richmond. Photostats of originals in Richmond County Court House.

Virginia, (Laws). *The Statutes at Large; Being a Collection of All the Laws of Virginia from the First Session of the Legislature, in the Year 1619.* William Waller Hening, ed. 13 vols. Richmond, 1810-1823.

Virginia, Richmond County. *Records.* State Library, Richmond. Photostats of originals in Richmond County Court House.

C. NEWSPAPERS

The Virginia Gazette (Williamsburg), 1736-1780.

D. PUBLISHED WRITINGS

Ballagh, James Curtis, ed., *The Letters of Richard Henry Lee.* 2 vols. New York: Macmillan Co., 1911-1914.

Fitzpatrick, John C., ed., *The Writings of George Washington from the Original Manuscript Sources 1745-1799.* 39 vols. Washington: Government Printing Office, 1931-1944.

Hamilton, Stanislaus Murray, ed., *Letters to Washington and Accompanying Papers.* 5 vols. Boston: Houghton-Mifflin, 1898-1902.

Wright, Louis B., ed., *Letters of Robert Carter, 1720-1727.* San Marino, California: The Huntington Library, 1940.

E. OTHER PUBLISHED WORKS

Bruce, Philip Alexander. *The Virginia Plutarch.* 2 vols. Chapel Hill: University of North Carolina Press, 1929.

———, ed. "The Will of John Carter," *Virginia Magazine of History and Biography*, II (1894), 235-236.

Bliss, Willard F. "The Rise of Tenancy in Virginia," *Virginia Magazine of History and Biography*, 58 (1950), 427-441.

Carter, Landon. "Observations on the Fly-Weevil, that destroys the wheat; with some useful discoveries and conclusions concerning the propagation and progress of that pernicious insect and the methods used for preventing the destruction of the grain by it," *The Transactions of the American Philosophical Society*. Philadelphia: The Society, I (1769), 167-185.

Carter, Robert Randolph, and Olive, Marion. *The Carter Family Tree*. Richmond: n.p., 1897.

Channing, Edward. *A History of the United States*. 6 vols. New York: Macmillan Co., 1907-1925.

Chitwood, Oliver Perry. *A History of Colonial America*. New York: Harper and Brothers, 1931.

Conway, Moncure Daniel. *Barons of the Potomac and the Rappahannock*. New York: The Grolier Club, 1892.

Eckenrode, H. J. *The Revolution in Virginia*. Boston: Houghton Mifflin Co., 1916.

Harrison, Fairfax. *Virginia Land Grants, A Study of Conveyancing in Relation to Colonial Politics*. Richmond: Old Dominion Press, 1925.

———. "Will of Charles Carter of Cleve," *Virginia Magazine of History and Biography*, XXXI (1923), 39-69.

Kearsley, G., ed. *American Gazette, Being a Collection of All the Authentic Addresses, Memorials, Letters, etc., Which Relate to the Present Dispute between Great Britain and Her Colonies, Containing also Many Original Papers Never Before Published*. 6 Numbers, London: G. Kearsley, 1768-1770.

Leake, James Miller. *The Virginia Committee System and the American Revolution*. Baltimore: Johns Hopkins University Press, 1917.

Lee, Edmund Jennings. *Lee of Virginia, 1642-1892*. Philadelphia: J. B. Lippincott & Co., 1895.

Main, Jackson T. "The One Hundred," *William and Mary College Quarterly*, ser. 3, XXI (1954), 354-384.

Miller, E. I. "The Virginia Committee of Correspondence 1759-1770," *William and Mary College Quarterly*, XXII (1913), 1-19.

Morton, Louis. *Robert Carter of Nomini Hall*. Princeton: Princeton University Press, 1941.

———. "Robert Wormeley Carter of Sabine Hall," *Journal of Southern History*, XII (1946), 345-365.

Stanard, Mary Newton. *Colonial Virginia, Its People and Customs*. Philadelphia: J. B. Lippincott & Co., 1917.

_____, and William G., comps. *The Colonial Virginia Register. A List of Governors, Councillors and Other High Officials, and Also of Members of the House of Burgesses and the Revolutionary Convention of the Colony of Virginia.* Albany: J. Munsell's Sons, 1902.

Stanard, William G., ed. "Carter Papers," *Virginia Magazine of History and Biography,* V (1898), 408-428, VI (1899), 1-18, VII (1900), 64-68.

_____. "Virginia Legislative Documents," *Virginia Magazine of History and Biography,* IX (1902), 353-368.

Tyler, Lyon G., ed. "The Diary of Landon Carter," *William and Mary College Quarterly,* ser. 1, XIII (1904), 45-53, 157-165, 219-224; XIV (1905), 38-44, 181-186, 246-253; XV (1906), 15-20, 63-69; XVI (1907), 149-156, 257-268; XVII (1908), 9-18.

_____. "The Leadership of Virginia in the War of the Revolution," *William and Mary College Quarterly,* ser. 1, XIX (1910), 10-25.

Van Tyne, Claude H. *The War of Independence.* 2 vols. Boston: Houghton Mifflin Co., 1928-1929.

Wertenbaker, Thomas Jefferson. *Patrician and Plebian in Virginia.* Charlottesville, Virginia: Michie Company, 1910.

_____. *The Old South: The Founding of American Civilization.* New York: Charles Scribner's Sons, 1942.

_____. *The Planters of Colonial Virginia.* Princeton: Princeton University Press, 1922.

Wharton, James. *King Carter the Man.* Kilmarnock, Virginia: *The Rappahannock Record,* 1950.

Wright, Louis B. *The First Gentlemen of Virginia, Intellectual Qualities of the Early Colonial Ruling Class.* San Marino, California: The Huntington Library, 1940.

INDEX

INDEX

[Numbers refer to items, not to pages. The introduction and biographical sketch are not indexed.]

G